Numerical Questions for National 5 Physics

Lyn Robinson

**Formerly Principal Teacher of Physics
Williamwood High School**

Published by
Chemcord
Inch Keith
East Kilbride
Glasgow

ISBN 9781870570282

Acknowledgement
Thanks to Jim Page, formerly Principal Teacher of
Physics at Queen Anne High School, Dunfermline for
his help in the editing of the early stages of this book.

Printed by Bell and Bain Ltd, Glasgow

Contents

Data Sheet

Speed of light in materials

Material	Speed in m s^{-1}
Air	3.0×10^8
Carbon dioxide	3.0×10^8
Diamond	1.2×10^8
Glass	2.0×10^8
Glycerol	2.1×10^8
Water	2.3×10^8

Speed of sound in materials

Material	Speed in m s^{-1}
Aluminium	5200
Air	340
Bone	4100
Carbon dioxide	270
Glycerol	1900
Muscle	1600
Steel	5200
Tissue	1500
Water	1500

Gravitational field strengths

Body	Gravitational field strength on the surface in N kg^{-1}
Earth	9.8
Jupiter	23
Mars	3.7
Mercury	3.7
Moon	1.6
Neptune	11
Saturn	9.0
Sun	270
Uranus	8.7
Venus	8.9

Radiation weighting factors

Type of radiation	Radiation weighting factor
alpha	20
beta	1
fast neutrons	10
gamma	1
slow neutrons	3

Melting and boiling points of materials

Material	Melting point in °C	Boiling point in °C
Alcohol	–98	65
Aluminium	660	2470
Copper	1077	2567
Glycerol	18	290
Lead	328	1737
Iron	1537	2737

Specific heat capacity of materials

Material	Specific heat capacity in $J\,kg^{-1}\,{}^{\circ}C^{-1}$
Alcohol	2350
Aluminium	902
Copper	386
Glass	500
Ice	2100
Iron	480
Lead	128
Oil	2130
Water	4180

Specific latent heat of fusion of materials

Material	Specific latent heat of fusion in $J\,kg^{-1}$
Alcohol	0.99×10^5
Aluminium	3.95×10^5
Carbon dioxide	1.80×10^5
Copper	2.05×10^5
Iron	2.67×10^5
Lead	0.25×10^5
Water	3.34×10^5

Specific latent heat of vaporisation of materials

Material	Specific latent heat of vaporisation in $J\,kg^{-1}$
Alcohol	11.20×10^5
Carbon dioxide	3.77×10^5
Glycerol	8.30×10^5
Turpentine	2.90×10^5
Water	22.6×10^5

Relationships

$$E_p = mgh$$

$$d = vt$$

$$E_k = \tfrac{1}{2}mv^2$$

$$v = f\lambda$$

$$Q = It$$

$$T = \frac{1}{f}$$

$$V = IR$$

$$A = \frac{N}{t}$$

$$R_T = R_1 + R_2 + R_3 + \ldots$$

$$D = \frac{E}{m}$$

$$\frac{1}{R_T} = \frac{1}{R_1} + \frac{1}{R_2} + \frac{1}{R_3} + \ldots$$

$$H = Dw_r$$

$$V_2 = \left(\frac{R_2}{R_1 + R_2}\right)V_s$$

$$\dot{H} = \frac{H}{t}$$

$$\frac{V_1}{V_2} = \frac{R_1}{R_2}$$

$$s = vt$$

$$P = \frac{E}{t}$$

$$d = \bar{v}t$$

$$P = IV$$

$$s = \bar{v}t$$

$$P = I^2 R$$

$$a = \frac{v - u}{t}$$

$$P = \frac{V^2}{R}$$

$$W = mg$$

$$E_h = cm\Delta T$$

$$F = ma$$

$$p = \frac{F}{A}$$

$$E_w = Fd$$

$$\frac{p_1 V_1}{T_1} = \text{constant}$$

$$E_h = ml$$

$$p_1 V_1 = p_2 V_2$$

$$\frac{p_1}{T_1} = \frac{p_2}{T_2}$$

$$\frac{V_1}{T_1} = \frac{V_2}{T_2}$$

Significant figures

In science, the number of significant figures determines the precision or accuracy of a number. For the answer to a calculation in physics to be completely meaningful, the number of significant figures should be no more than the least number of figures in a value used in the calculation.

Example
When you multiply 42.3 (3 significant figures) by 2.7 (3 significant figures), the answer shown on the calculator is 114.21.
The answer given to the fewest number of significant figures (two) is 110.

In the National 5 Physics examination, it is acceptable for the number of significant figures in the answer to a calculation to be two more or one less than the value with the fewest figures. This the guiding principle used in providing the answers to the questions in this book.

The following examples illustrate the approach used in this book.

Examples
Calculation : 6 x 14	Answer in book:	84	(calculator 84)
Calculation : 21 x 37	Answer in book:	777	(calculator 777)
Calculation : 58 x 233	Answer in book:	1334	(calculator 1334)
Calculation : (42 x 23) / 2.7	Answer in book:	358	(calculator 357.777...)
Calculation : $\sqrt{4.4 \times 2.0 \times 18}$	Answer in book:	13	(calculator 12.5857...)
Calculation : $\sqrt{2.3 \times 4.0}$	Answer in book:	3	(calculator 3.03315...)

Prefixes

The SI system of units is based on powers of ten and uses a system of prefixes that indicate the multiple or sub-unit being used.

You should know the following prefixes.

nano (n)	10^{-9}		giga (G)	10^{9}
micro (μ)	10^{-6}		mega (M)	10^{6}
milli (m)	10^{-3}		kilo (k)	10^{3}

DYNAMICS

Speed, distance and time

1. a) Convert 90 km h^{-1} to m s^{-1}.

   b) Convert 35 m s^{-1} to km h^{-1}

2. a) State the equation that links **speed** with **distance** and **time**.

   b) State the symbol for each quantity.

   c) State the unit for each quantity, and its abbreviation.

3. Calculate the average speed of each of the following, in m s^{-1}.

   a) A trolley that travels 12 m in 10 s.

   b) A car that travels 48 km in 50 minutes.

   c) A plane that travels 3100 km in 3 hours.

4. Calculate the time for each of the following.

   a) A walker who moves at an average speed of 1.4 m s^{-1} to travel 224 m.

   b) A bus that moves at an average speed of 12 m s^{-1} to travel 15 km.

   c) Sound to travel a distance of 7.5 m through water.

   (Use the speed of sound shown in the Data Sheet on pages i and ii.)

5. Calculate the distance covered by each of the following.

   a) A toy car moving at an average speed of 0.24 m s^{-1} in 15 s.

   b) A bullet moving at an average speed of 280 m s^{-1} in 0.20 s.

   c) Light to travel through air in 15 ns.

   (Use the speed of light in air shown in the Data Sheet on pages i and ii.)

6. A runner completes 10 km in 40 minutes.

   Calculate the runner's average speed:

   a) in km h^{-1};

   b) in m s^{-1}.

7. A trolley with a 50 mm card attached to it is released from point **A**. The trolley runs down the slope with a constant acceleration, passing through a light gate at point **B**.

Time from point **A** to point **B**   =   7.5 s
Time on light gate timer   =   0.025 s

a) Calculate the average speed between points **A** and **B**, in m s⁻¹.

b) Calculate the instantaneous speed of the trolley at point **B**, in m s⁻¹.

8.

A ball bearing, placed at point **A**, starts from rest and rolls down the slope with a constant acceleration to point **B** in 2.5 s. The speed of the ball at point **B** is 0.12 m s⁻¹.

a) Calculate the average speed of the ball from point **A** to point **B**.

b) Calculate the distance *d*.

Vector and scalar quantities

1. Calculate the final displacement for travel:

   a) in a direction of 30 m due east, followed by 55 m due west;

   b) in a direction of 45 m due east, followed by 70 m due east;

   c) in a direction of 500 m due north, followed by 2.5 km due south.

2. A girl walks from point X to point Y along a winding road.
   Point Y is 3.0 km due east of point X. She took 30 minutes for her walk.
   The road between points X and Y is 4.6 km long.

   a) i) What distance does she walk?

      ii) What is her displacement at the end of her walk?

   b) i) Calculate her average speed, in m s^{-1}.

      ii) Calculate her average velocity, in m s^{-1}.

3. An athlete completes a 400 m race on an oval track in a time of 65 s.
   The race starts and finishes at the same place.

   a) i) What distance is travelled by the athlete?

      ii) What is the final displacement of the athlete?

   b) i) Calculate the athlete's average speed for the race, in m s^{-1}.

      ii) What is the athlete's average velocity for the race?

4. A car travels 54 km due north, then turns due south for 68 km with the journey taking 2 hours.

   a) i) What distance does the car travel?

      ii) What is the final displacement of the car?

   b) i) Calculate the average speed of the car, in km h^{-1}.

      ii) Calculate the average velocity of the car, in km h^{-1}.

5. A car travels 90 km due north and then turns due east for 120 km.
   The journey takes 2.5 hours.

   a) i) What distance does the car travel?

      ii) What is the final displacement of the car?

   b) i) Calculate the average speed of the car, in km h^{-1}.

      ii) Calculate the average velocity of the car, in km h^{-1}.

6. Draw a scale diagram and use it to find the final displacement for each of the following.

   Give both the magnitude and the direction of the displacement.

   a) A walker travels 400 m due north and then 300 m due east.

   b) A mouse that runs 5.0 m due east and then 12 m due north.

   c) A student travels 900 m due south and then 400 m due west.

7. Calculate the final displacement (both magnitude and direction) for each of the following.

   a) A ship sails 12 km due south and then 9.0 km due east.

   b) A car travels 25 km due west and then 18 km due south.

   c) An orienteer runs 62 m due west and then 75 m due north.

8. By drawing a scale diagram or otherwise, calculate the final displacement (both magnitude and direction) for the motion of each of the following remote-controlled cars.

   a) A car that moves 3.0 m due east, then 1.5 m due south, followed by 1.0 m due west.

   b) A car that moves 4.6 m due south, then 2.0 m due west, followed by 2.3 m due north.

   c) A car that moves 12 m due south, then 2.0 m due west, followed by 1.2 m due north.

Acceleration

1. a) State the equation that links **acceleration** with **initial velocity, final velocity** and **time**.
    b) State the symbol for each quantity.
    c) State the unit for each quantity, and its abbreviation.

2. Calculate the acceleration of each of the following objects travelling in a straight line.
    a) A car that starts from rest and reaches a speed of 15 m s^{-1} in 6.0 s.
    b) An athlete who reaches a speed of 9.0 m s^{-1}, off the starting blocks, in 2.0 s.
    c) A car that has an initial speed of 22 m s^{-1}; it accelerates for 6.0 s to reach a speed of 31 m s^{-1}.
    d) A charged particle that enters an electric field with an initial speed of 300 m s^{-1} and reaches a speed of 5900 m s^{-1} in 7.0 s.
    e) A rocket has an initial speed of 1200 m s^{-1}; when the rocket engine fires for 40 s the speed increases to 2480 m s^{-1}
    f) A trolley that moves with an initial speed of 0.80 m s^{-1}; after 2.0 s the speed of the trolley is 0.48 m s^{-1}.
    g) An oil tanker that takes 25 minutes to stop from an initial speed of 4.0 m s^{-1}.
    h) A car that reaches a speed of 35 m s^{-1} from rest in 4.2 s.
    i) A space shuttle that reaches a speed of 1200 m s^{-1} in a time of 48 s after launch.
    j) A racing car that has an initial speed of 35 m s^{-1}; it accelerates for 7.2 s to reach a speed of 84 m s^{-1}.
    k) A train that takes 12 s to come to a stop from a speed of 88 m s^{-1}.
    l) A bullet that is moving with a speed of 280 m s^{-1}; it hits a wall stopping in 0.25 s.

3. Calculate the time taken for each of the following.
    a) A car moving at a speed of 30 m s^{-1} that decelerates at 4.0 m s^{-2} to a stop.
    b) A plane that accelerates at 18 m s^{-2} from rest along the runway until it reaches the take-off speed of 81 m s^{-1}.
    c) A car that accelerates at 9.5 m s^{-2} from 0 to 60 mph (0 to 27 m s^{-1}).

4. Calculate the final speed for each of the following.

   a) A motorbike that accelerates at 2.5 m s^{-2}, from rest, for 10 s.

   b) A cruise liner that accelerates at 0.0035 m s^{-2}, from rest, for 42 minutes.

   c) An athlete who is running at 9.8 m s^{-1} and decelerates at 2.0 m s^{-2} for 3.0 s.

5. Calculate the initial speed of each of the following

   a) A van that accelerates at 1.5 m s^{-2} for 4.0 s and reaches a speed of 22 m s^{-1}.

   b) A car that accelerates at 2.2 m s^{-2} for 5.0 s and reaches a speed of 32 m s^{-1}.

   c) A bus that decelerates at 1.8 m s^{-2} for 5.0 s and reaches a speed of 8.0 m s^{-1}.

6. A toy car starting from rest reaches a speed of 3.0 m s^{-1} in 4.0 s.

   a) Calculate the acceleration of the car.

   b) Calculate the time taken for the car to reach a speed of 9.0 m s^{-1} from rest.

7. A stone is dropped over a cliff. The stone hits the ground 3.7 s later. The acceleration due to gravity is 9.8 m s^{-2}.

   a) Calculate the time for the dropped stone to reach a speed of 7.0 m s^{-1}.

   b) What is its speed on striking the ground?

8. A car has a maximum acceleration of 3.4 m s^{-2}.

   a) Calculate the maximum speed of the car after 5.0 s.

   b) Calculate the minimum time taken for the car to reach a speed of 27 m s^{-1} from rest.

9. During a safety test a car has to run into a wall at a speed of 31 m s^{-1}. The car accelerates at 5.0 m s^{-2} from rest.

   a) Calculate the time taken for the car to reach the wall.

   b) On hitting the wall, the car comes to a stop in 160 ms.

   Calculate the deceleration of the car on hitting the wall.

10. The maximum deceleration that the brakes of a car can safely produce is 7.5 m s^{-2}. A driver in the car applies the brakes when the speed of the car is 70 mph (31 m s^{-1}).

   Calculate the minimum time taken for the car to stop.

Velocity (speed) – time graphs

1. Describe the motion represented in each of the following graphs.

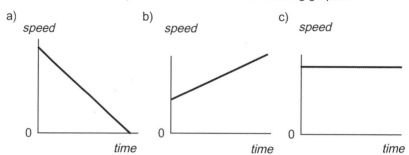

a)

speed

time

b)

speed

time

c)

speed

time

2. Sketch the speed-time graph for the following motion of an athlete in a race.
   For the first 2.0 s of the race, the athlete accelerates uniformly from rest.
   During the next 3.0 s, the athlete continues to accelerate but at a lower rate.
   The athlete continues for 5.0 s at a constant speed.
   Finally, the athlete declerates for 4.0 s to come to rest after crossing the finishing line.

   (Values are needed on the time axis but not on the speed axis.)

3. The graph shows the way that the speed of a car varies over a 50 s period.

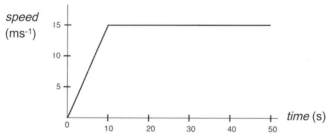

   speed (ms⁻¹)

   a) Describe the motion of the car.
   b) Calculate the initial accleration of the car.
   c) Calculate the total distance travelled by the car in the 50 s.

4. A car starts from rest and accelerates at 3.0 m s⁻² for 7.0 s. It then travels at a constant speed for 15 s, finally slowing steadily to a halt in 8.0 s.

   a) Calculate the maximum speed of the car.
   b) Draw the speed-time graph for the motion of the car.
   c) Calculate the total distance that the car travels.

5. Consider the following speed-time graphs for the motion of an object.

i)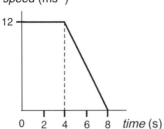

ii)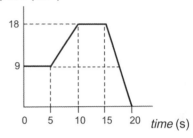

iii)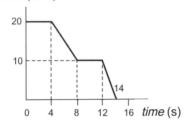

a) Calculate the total distance travelled by each object.

b) Calculate the average speed of each object.

6. The speed-time graph represents the motion of a remote-controlled car.

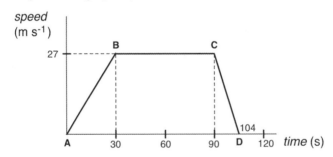

a) Between which two points is the vehicle travelling at a constant speed?

b) i) Calculate the intial acceleration of the car.

    ii) Calculate the final acceleration of the car.

c) Calculate the braking distance of the car.

d) i) Calculate the total distance travelled by the car.

    ii) Calculate the average speed of the car.

7. The speed-time graph represents the motion of a cyclist.

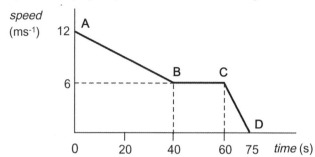

a) Describe the motion of the cyclist:

i) represented by section **AB**;

ii) represented by section **BC**;

iii) represented by section **CD**.

b) Calculate the acceleration of the cyclist:

i) represented by section **AB**;

ii) represented by section **CD**.

c) Calculate the total distance covered by the cyclist during the journey.

8. Consider the speed-time graph for the motion of a remote-controlled car.

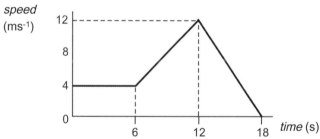

a) Describe the motion of the car during the 18 s.

b) Calculate the acceleration of the car:

i) between 6.0 s and 12 s;

ii) between 12 s and 18 s.

c) Calculate the speed of the car:

i) 9.0 s from the start;

ii) 15 s from the start.

d) Calculate the total distance travelled by the car during the 18 s.

9. A rocket accelerates from 10 m s⁻¹ to 60 m s⁻¹ in 4.0 s, and then maintains this steady speed for 7.0 s.
    It then accelerates again for 5.0 s at 8.0 m s⁻².
    It maintains this steady speed for a further 4.0 s, and then decelerates to rest in 10 s.
    a) Draw a speed-time graph for the motion of the rocket.
    b) Calculate the total distance travelled by the rocket.

10. The velocity-time graph represents the motion of a remote-controlled car.

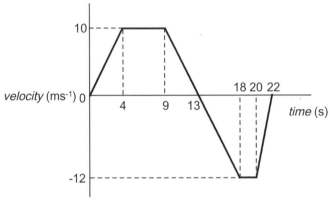

    a) Describe the motion of the car.
    b) i)   Calculate the initial acceleration of the car.
        ii) Calculate the acceleration of the car between 13 s and 18 s.
        iii) Calculate the final acceleration of the car.
    c) i)   Calculate the total distance travelled by the car.
        ii) Calculate the final displacement of the car.

11. A car accelerates from rest at 3.0 m s⁻² for 6.0 s, and then continues at a constant velocity for 4.0 s. It comes to rest in another 5.0 s.
    After a further 3.0 s it accelerates in the opposite direction at 2.5 m s⁻² for 4.0 s, and then continues at a constant velocity for 6.0 s. It comes to rest 2.0 s later.
    a) Calculate each of the two constant velocities of the car.
    b) Draw the velocity-time graph for the motion of the car.
    c) i)   Calculate the total distance travelled by the car.
        ii) Calculate the final displacement of the car.

12. The velocity-time graph represents the motion of a helicopter.

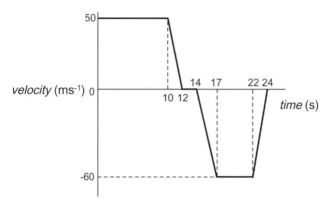

a)   Describe the motion of the helicopter.

b)   i)   Calculate the initial deceleration of the helicopter.

     ii)   Calculate the acceleration of the helicopter between 14 s and 17 s.

     iii) Calculate the final deceleration of the helicopter.

c)   i)   Calculate the total distance travelled by the helicopter.

     ii)   Calculate the final displacement of the helicopter.

13. A ball, dropped from the top of a building takes 2.5 s to reach a top speed of 24 m s^{-1} just before hitting the ground.

a)   Use this data to calculate the acceleration due to gravity.

b)   Draw a speed-time graph to represent the motion of the ball (numbers required on both axes).

c)   Calculate the height of the building.

14. A ball is thrown vertically upwards with an initial speed of 19.6 m s^{-1}.

a)   i)   What is the vertical acceleration as the ball travels up?

     ii)   What is the vertical acceleration as the ball travels down?

b)   Calculate the time taken by the ball to reach the top of the flight.

c)   What is the vertical speed of the ball as it falls back into the hand?

d)   Draw a velocity-time graph to represent the motion of the ball (numbers required on both axes).

e)   i)   Calculate is the total distance travelled by the ball.

     ii)   What is the final displacement of the ball?

Weight

For some of the questions in this section, you will have to use the information from the table 'Gravitational field strengths' shown in the Data Sheet on pages i and ii.

1. a) State the equation that links **weight** with **mass**, and **gravitational field strength**.

   b) State the symbol for each quantity.

   c) State the unit for each quantity, and its abbreviation.

2. Calculate the weight of each of the following.

   a) A stone with a mass of 2.5 kg, on Earth.

   b) A vehicle with a mass of 2300 kg, on the Moon.

3. Calculate the mass of each of the following.

   a) A brick with a weight of 150 N, on Earth.

   b) A space probe with a weight of 1300 N, on Jupiter.

4. An object with a mass of 2.5 kg has a weight of 24.5 N on solar system body **A**; an object with a mass of 107 kg has a weight of 171 N on solar system body **B**.

   a) Calculate the gravitational field strength on each of the **two** bodies.

   b) Identify each of the **two** bodies.

5. An object has a mass of 65 kg on Earth.

   a) Calculate the weight of the object on Earth.

   b) i) What would be the mass of the object on Jupiter?

      ii) Calculate the weight that the object would have on Jupiter.

6. An object has a weight of 199 N on Earth.

   a) Calculate the mass of the object on Earth.

   b) i) What is the mass of the object on Mars?

      ii) Calculate the weight that the object would have on Mars.

7. The weight of rock samples on the Moon was 64 N.

   Calculate the weight of the samples on Earth.

Resultant quantities

For all questions in this section, in your answer give both the **magnitude** and **direction** of the resultant force.

1. Calculate the resultant of the forces for each of the following.

a) 3 N   5 N   b) 4 N   8 N

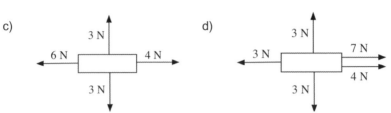

c)   3 N   d)   3 N

6 N   4 N   3 N   7 N

3 N   4 N

3 N

2. Calculate the resultant of the forces for each of the following.

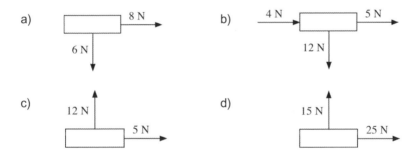

a)   8 N   b)   4 N   5 N

6 N   12 N

c)   12 N   d)   15 N

5 N   25 N

3. Calculate the resultant force on each of the following.

a) A ship that is sailing with an engine force due north of 8.0×10^5 N is moving in a current due east, producing a force of 3.0×10^5 N on the ship.

b) A boat has two ropes attached. One rope exerts a force of 120 N on a bearing 045. The other rope exerts a force of 120 N on a bearing 135.

4. Calculate the resultant velocity for each of the following.

   a) A plane that is flying at a velocity of 220 m s^{-1} as a result of an engine force due north is experiencing a strong wind of 50 m s^{-1} due west.

   b) A boat that is travelling with a velocity of 15 m s^{-1} as a result of an engine force due east is moving in a current that has a velocity of 7.0 m s^{-1} due south.

5. A rocket on the launch-pad has a mass of 30 kg.
   On take-off, the engine force vertically is 800 N.

   a) Calculate the weight of the rocket.

   b) Sketch a diagram, showing the forces acting on the rocket on take-off.
      (The forces should be named and their magnitude shown.)

   c) Calculate the resultant force on the rocket.

Newton's First Law

1. State Newton's First Law.

2. When the engine force on a car is 16 kN, it travels at a constant speed of 23 m s^{-1}.
   a) What is the frictional force that is acting on the car?
   b) Calculate the distance that the car travels in 5 minutes.

3. A block of mass 28 kg is suspended from a rope at a building site.
   Calculate the magnitude of the tension in the rope.

4. A balloon of mass 2.5 kg rises with a constant velocity of 17 m s^{-1}.
   a) Calculate the upwards force caused by the air.
   b) Calculate the height gained by the balloon in 40 s.

5. A rocket is fired from Earth and reaches a maximum speed of 17 km s^{-1}. The engines are then switched off.
   What is the velocity of the rocket 24 hours later?

6. An object is pulled vertically by a constant force of 275 N. The object has a constant speed of 15 m s^{-1}.
   a) What is the weight of the object?
   b) Calculate the mass of the object.

7. An object is pulled vertically by a constant force of 147 N. The object has a constant speed of 36 m s^{-1}.
   Calculate the mass of the object.

Newton's Second Law

1. State Newton's Second Law.

2. a) State the equation that links **force** with **mass** and **acceleration**.

   b) State the symbol for each quantity.

   c) State the unit for each quantity, and its abbreviation.

3. Calculate the resultant force that is acting on each of the following.

   a) A 300 g object that accelerates at 15 m s^{-2}.

   b) A 3.0 kg block that accelerates at 2.4 m s^{-2}.

   c) A 2100 kg vehicle that accelerates at 0.13 m s^{-2}.

4. Calculate the acceleration produced by each of the following.

   a) A resultant force of 18 N applied to an object of mass 100 g.

   b) A resultant force of 210 N applied to a trolley of mass 2.5 kg.

   c) A resultant force of 6.2 kN applied to an car of mass 1500 kg.

5. Calculate the mass of each of the following.

   a) A toy car that accelerates at 15 m s^{-2} due to a resultant force of 50 N.

   b) An object that accelerates at 0.13 m s^{-2} due to a resultant force of 520 N.

   c) A vehicle that accelerates at 16 m s^{-2} due to a resultant force of 208 kN.

6. A balloon has a mass of 3.5 kg.
   The resultant force on the balloon is 70 N upwards.

   Calculate the acceleration of the balloon.

7. A car, mass 1040 kg, accelerates at 2.75 m s^{-2}.

   Calculate the resultant force acting on the car.

8. A rocket accelerates from the Earth's surface at 25 m s^{-2} due to a resultant force of 1500 kN.

   Calculate the mass of the rocket.

9. A van of mass 900 kg on a horizontal straight road accelerates from rest to a final speed of 22 m s^{-1} in 8.0 s.

   a) Calculate the acceleration of the van.

   b) Calculate the resultant force acting on the van.

10. A trolley of mass 2.5 kg is pulled by a force of 17 N.
    There is a frictional force of 4.5 N on the trolley.

    Calculate the acceleration of the trolley.

11. An engine force of 2 kN applied to car produces an acceleration of 2.5 m s^{-2}.
    The frictional force on the car is 300 N.

    Calculate the mass of the car.

12. An engine force of 750 N applied to a car of mass 280 kg produces an acceleration of 2.25 m s^{-2}.

    Calculate the frictional force acting on the car.

13. A toy car, mass 3.0 kg, accelerates at 0.50 m s^{-2}.
    The frictional force acting on the car is 2.0 N.

    Calculate the engine force of the car .

For question 14, you will have to use the information from the table 'Gravitational field strengths' shown in the Data Sheet on pages i and ii.

14. A rocket of mass 2.5 x 10^6 kg accelerates vertically from the surface the Moon. The rocket engine produces a total force of 3.8 x 10^7 N.

    a) Calculate the weight of the rocket.

    b) Calculate the acceleration of the rocket.

Newton's Third Law

1. State Newton's Third law.

2. The force on the foot of an athlete as she pushes off the starting block is 300 N.

   What is the force of her foot on the block?

3. A footballer kicks a ball of mass 400 g, giving it a momentary horizontal acceleration of 375 m s^{-2}.

   a) Calculate the force on the ball.

   b) What is the force on the foot of the footballer?

4. Two skaters are standing together in the centre of an ice rink.
   Paul has a mass of 75 kg and his friend Jenna has a mass of 58 kg.
   Jenna pushes Paul and he accelerates away from her at a speed of 1.8 m s^{-2}.

   a) Calculate the force that Jenna exerts on Paul.

   b) What force will Jenna experience?

   c) Calculate Jenna's acceleration.

Work done

1. a) State the equation that links **work done** with **force** and **distance**.

   b) State the symbol for each quantity.

   c) State the unit for each quantity, and its abbreviation.

2. Calculate the work done by each of the following forces.

   a) A 6.0 N force moving an object a distance of 7.5 m.

   b) A 30 kN force moving an object a distance of 400 m.

   c) A 0.012 N force moving an object a distance of 7.5×10^{-4} m.

3. Calculate the force acting on each of the following objects.

   a) When the force supplies 750 J of energy to move the object a distance of 25 m.

   b) When the force supplies 675 kJ of energy to move the object a distance of 150 m.

   c) When the force supplies 56 MJ of energy to move the object a distance of 40 km.

4. Calculate the distance moved by the object in each of the following.

   a) A 47 N force transfers 58 750 J of energy to move the object.

   b) A 3.6×10^6 N force transfers 3.312×10^9 J of energy to move the object.

   c) A 2.75×10^{-3} N force transfers 330 J of energy to move the object.

5. A train engine exerts 15 000 N to pull a train a distance of 600 m.
   Calculate the work done by this force.

6. A worker does 3600 J of work pushing a trolley with a force of 300 N.
   Calculate the distance moved by the trolley .

7. The work done by a student in pulling a heavy load for 30 m is 7200 kJ.
   Calculate the force applied by the student.

8. The work done by a weightlifter in lifting a barbell is 4.8 kJ.
   The force exerted to lift the barbell in 2500 N.

   Calculate the height to which the barbell is raised.

9. A train engine pulls the coaches with a steady force of 500 kN. The train travels a distance of 3.0 km.

Calculate the work done by the engine during this time.

10. A gardener pushes a wheelbarrow with a force of 350 N.

Calculate the work that is done by this force in moving the wheelbarrow through a distance of 25 m.

11. A man weighing 800 N climbs stairs to his flat. The stairs are 30 m high.

Calculate the work done by the man in climbing the stairs.

12. A pram is pushed with a force of 75 N. The work done by this force is 90 kJ.

Calculate the distance moved by the pram.

Power, work done and time

1. a) State the equation that links **power** with **work done** and **time**.

   b) State the symbol for each quantity.

   c) State the unit for each quantity, and its abbreviation.

2. Calculate the power required for each of the following.

   a) To do 18 J of work for 10 s.

   b) To do 220 kJ of work for 5.0 s.

   c) To do 7.2×10^3 J of work for 1 minute.

3. Calculate the work done by each of the following.

   a) A power of 360 W for 10 s.

   b) A power of 30 W for 2 minutes.

   c) A power of 2.5 kW for 200 s.

4. Calculate the time that it takes for each of the following.

   a) A power of 240 W to do 6000 J of work.

   b) A power of 260 W to do 5.2×10^5 J of work.

   c) A power of 6.4×10^3 kW to do 160 MJ of work.

5. Calculate the power of a boy who does 1540 J of work when pushing a wheelbarrow for 44 s.

6. The energy used by a worker in pushing a box across a floor is 400 J. The box is pushed for 5.5 s.

   Calculate the power in pushing the box.

7. The power of a mechanic who is pushing a car into a garage is 40 W. The energy used is 1.2 kJ.

   Calculate the time taken to push the car.

8. A lift moves upwards as a result of a force of 1.2×10^6 N. The lift takes 4.0 s to rise from one floor to the next, a distance of 12 m.

   Calculate the power of the lift.

Gravitational potential energy

1. a) State the equation that links **gravitational potential energy** with **mass, gravitational field strength** and **height**.

   b) State the symbol for each quantity.

   c) State the unit for each quantity, and its abbreviation.

2. Calculate the gain in gravitational potential energy for each of the following.

   a) A ball of mass 17 kg raised through a height of 5.3 m.

   b) A book of mass 85 g raised through a height of 130 mm.

   c) A helicopter of mass 6310 kg raised through a height of 8.0 km.

3. Calculate the mass of each of the following.

   a) A box that gains a gravitational potential energy of 150 J when raised through a height of 3.0 m.

   b) A book that gains a gravitational potential energy of 34 J when raised through a height of 40 m.

   c) A glider that gains a gravitational potential energy of 4.9×10^8 MJ when raised through a height of 2.0 km.

4. Calculate the height gained by lifting each of the following.

   a) A rock with a mass of 8.2 kg; the gain in gravitational potential energy is 1240 J.

   b) A block of wood with a mass of 610 g; the gain in gravitational potential energy is 15 J.

   c) A crate with a mass of 27 kg; the gain in gravitational potential energy is 9500 J.

5. A lift gains 1250 kJ of gravitational potential energy when rising to a height of 84 m.

   Calculate the mass of the lift.

6. A student of mass 58.5 kg climbs the 247 steps of the Scott Monument in Edinburgh. In doing so, the student gains 36.0 kJ of gravitational potential energy.

   Calculate the height gained by the student.

7. An astronaut of mass 65 kg gains 2288 J of gravitational potential energy when climbing to a height of 22 m on the Moon.

    Calculate the gravitational field strength on the Moon.

8. A brick of mass 795 g is raised on to a platform 25 m above the ground.

    Calculate the gravitational potential energy that is gained by the brick.

9. Calculate the gravitational potential energy a 40 kg boy would have gained at a height of 25 m when on a fun-ride.

Kinetic energy

1. a) State the equation that links **kinetic energy** with **mass** and **speed**.
   b) State the symbol for each quantity.
   c) State the unit for each quantity, and its abbreviation.

2. Calculate the kinetic energy of each of the following.
   a) A toy car of mass 4.0 kg moving at a speed of 3.0 m s^{-1}.
   b) A runner of mass 75 kg moving at a speed of 8.0 m s^{-1}.
   c) A bullet of mass 5.2 g moving at a speed of 150 m s^{-1}.

3. Calculate the mass of each of the following.
   a) A bowling ball moving at a speed of 2.0 m s^{-1} with a kinetic energy of 7.6 J.
   b) A car moving at a speed of 15 m s^{-1} with a kinetic energy of 169 kJ.
   c) A cannon shell moving at a speed of 140 m s^{-1} with a kinetic energy of 4.0 x 10^4 J.

4. Calculate the speed of each of the following.
   a) A skier of mass 80 kg moving with a kinetic energy of 5760 J.
   b) A boulder of mass 4.0 kg moving with a kinetic energy of 450 J.
   c) A train of mass 3.2 x 10^5 kg moving with a kinetic energy of 1.35 x 10^8 J.

5. A vehicle is travelling at a speed of 20 m s^{-1} with a kinetic energy of 200 kJ.
   Calculate the mass of the vehicle.

6. A motor cyclist and his bike have a total mass of 360 kg.
   They have a combined kinetic energy of 87 120 J.
   Calculate the speed of the bike.

7. A trolley of mass 0.21 kg is moving at 1.6 m s^{-1}.
   Calculate the kinetic energy of the trolley.

8. a) i) A toy car of mass 6.0 kg has a speed of 5.0 m s⁻¹.

   Calculate the kinetic energy of the car.

   ii) The car doubles its speed to 10 m s⁻¹.

   Calculate its new kinetic energy.

   b) i) A rocket of mass 700 kg has a speed of 75 m s⁻¹.

   Calculate the kinetic energy of the rocket.

   ii) The rocket doubles its speed to 150 m s⁻¹.

   Calculate its new kinetic energy.

   c) What happens to the value of the kinetic energy of an object when its speed doubles?

9. In 2009, Usain Bolt set a world record of 9.58 seconds for the 100 m sprint.

   Calculate his average kinetic energy for the run.

   (Assume his mass to be 94.1 kg.)

Mixed dynamic problems (i)

1. A toy plane has a mass of 1.5 kg. On gaining a height of 60 m, the plane is flying with a speed of 14 m s^{-1}.

    a) i) Calculate the gravitational potential energy of the plane.

        ii) Calculate the kinetic energy of the plane.

    b) What is the total energy of the plane?

2. A runner of mass 60 kg taking part in a marathon is travelling at a speed of 4.2 m s^{-1}. The runner has climbed 30 m vertically since the start of the race.

    a) i) Calculate the gravitational potential energy gained by the runner.

        ii) Calculate the kinetic energy of the runner.

    b) What is total energy of the runner?

3. A ball of mass 100 g is dropped from the top of a tower 287 m tall.

    a) Calculate the gravitational potential energy of the ball on the top of the tower.

    b) i) What is the kinetic energy of the ball just before hitting the ground?

        ii) Calculate the speed of the ball as it hits the ground.

    c) What assumption is made in this calculation?

4. A toy wagon of mass 2.5 kg starts from rest and runs down a slope.

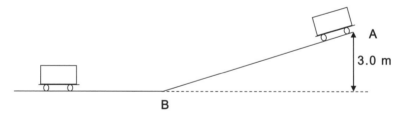

    a) Calculate the gravitational potential energy lost moving from point **A** to point **B**.

    b) i) What is the maximum kinetic energy of the wagon at point **B**?

        ii) Calculate the maximum speed of the wagon at point **B**.

5. A van of mass 1200 kg is parked on a hill but the brakes are faulty. The vertical height of the hill is 8.0 m. The slipping brakes heat up as the car runs to the bottom of the hill, crashing into a wall at 9.0 m s^{-1}.

   a) Calculate the gravitational potential energy lost by the car.

   b) Calculate the kinetic energy of the car as it hits the wall.

   c) Assuming no loss of energy due to friction with the road, what is the heat energy produced in the brake pads?

6. A ball of mass 400 g rolls across a table at a speed of 2.5 m s^{-1}.
   The table is 1.5 m high.
   The ball rolls off the table at point X and lands at point Y.

   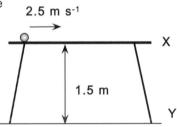

   a) i) Calculate the initial gravitational potential energy of the ball.

      ii) Calculate the kinetic energy of the ball at point X.

      iii) What is the total energy at point X?

   b) Calculate the maximum speed of the ball at point Y.

7. A ball of mass 25 g is thrown vertically up with a speed of 15 m s^{-1}.

   a) Calculate the kinetic energy of the ball as it leaves the hand of the thrower.

   b) Calculate the maximum height gained by the ball.

8. A boy of mass 40 kg climbs onto a diving board that is 10 m above the water. He then dives in.

   Calculate his maximum speed on entering the water.

9. A package is dropped from a helicopter that is hovering at a height of 950 m.

   Calculate the maximum speed of the package just before it hits the ground.

10. A ball falls off a cliff that is 125 m high.

    Calculate the maximum speed of the ball as it hits the ground.

Mixed dynamics problems (ii)

1. A car of mass 1200 kg is travelling at 20 m s^{-1}.
    The braking force is 5.0 kN.
    a) Calculate the kinetic energy of the car.
    b) Calculate the minimum braking distance.

2. A machine lifts a load of 5000 N to a height of 8 m in 20 s.
    Calculate the minimum power of the machine.

3. While raising a load, a lift operates with a power output of 12 kW for 105 s.
    Calculate the minimum work done in raising the load.

4. Child **A** with a mass of 35 kg runs up stairs of vertical height 14 m in 15 s.
    Child **B** with a mass of 30 kg takes 10 s to run up the same stairs.
    a) Do the children do equal or different amounts of work?
        Justify your answer.
    b) i)   Calculate the power of child **A**.
        ii) Calculate the power of child **B**.

5. Student **A** takes 12 s to lift 75 kg up three flights of stairs, a total height of
    21 m. Student **B** carries an identical mass up the same stairs but takes 15 s.
    a) i)   How does the power of student **A** compare to student **B**?
        ii) How does the work done by student **A** compare to student **B**?
    b) Calculate the average power of student **A**.

6. A tractor applies a force of 2600 N to pull a trailer for 150 m in 30 s.
    a) Calculate the work done by the tractor to pull the trailer.
    b) Calculate the useful power output of the tractor.

7. A lift can raise a total mass of 1.8 x 10^4 kg up 25 m in 40 s.
    Calculate the minimum power of the lift.

8. A load of 700 kg is lifted 28 m in a time of 18 s.
    a) Calculate the potential energy that is supplied to the load.
    b) Calculate the minimum power of motor that is required.

9. A 55 kg girl on a 17 kg bicycle is moving at a steady speed of 9.0 m s⁻¹. She applies the brakes on her bicycle and it comes to rest in 3.5 s.

   a) Calculate the kinetic energy of the girl plus her bicycle before she applies the brakes.

   b) Calculate the minimum power of the brakes.

10. A lift carries 15 people with an average mass of 70 kg. The mass of the lift itself is 700 kg. It travels up 80 floors in 2 minutes. Each floor is 4.2 m high.

    a) i) What is the total mass of the full lift?

       ii) What is the total height travelled by the lift?

    b) Calculate the gain in potential energy.

    c) i) Calculate the minimum power of the lift.

       ii) Why would the actual power have to be greater than the calculated power?

11. A weightlifter lifts a mass of 280 kg from the ground to a height of 1.6 m in a time of 1.8 s.

    Calculate the average power of the weightlifter during the lift.

12. A bucket of water of weight 280 N is lifted up a 40 m well by a 750 W motor.

    Calculate the minimum time taken to raise the bucket.

13. A 39 kg child on a 20 kg bicycle is moving at a steady speed of 11 m s⁻¹. The brakes are applied and the bicycle comes to rest after a distance of 8.0 m.

    a) Calculate the kinetic energy of the child plus the bicycle before braking.

    b) Calculate the average force of the brakes.

14. An electric motor on a lift raises a load of 9000 N at a steady speed of 3.5 m s⁻¹ in 12 s.

    Calculate the minimum power of the motor.

15. A carriage of a roller coaster travels through a vertical height of 18 m on a section of track that is 25 m long. The mass of the carriage is 2200 kg.

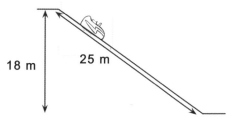

18 m   25 m

a) i) Calculate the maximum kinetic energy of the carriage at the bottom of the slope.

ii) Calculate the maximum speed of the carriage at the bottom of the slope.

b) The actual value of its kinetic energy at the bottom of the slope is 220 kJ.

i) How much energy was used to overcome friction?

ii) Calculate the average force of friction that was acting.

iii) Calculate the actual speed of the carriage at the bottom of the slope.

16. A rocket engine produces a force of 941 N.
The rocket has a mass of 43 kg.

a) Calculate the weight of the rocket on Earth.

b) Sketch a diagram showing the forces acting on the rocket on take-off. The forces should be named and their magnitude shown.

c) Calculate the acceleration of the rocket.

17. A trolley of mass 1.8 kg is pulled from rest by a rope along a straight level track with a force of 8.1 N.

(Assume that the frictional force is negligible.)

a) Calculate the acceleration of the trolley.

b) i) Calculate is the velocity after 4.0 s.

ii) The 8.1 N force is removed after 4.0 s.

What is the velocity after 7.0 s?

18. The lunar vehicle, mass 750 kg, has a top speed of 5.0 km h^{-1}.

    a)   i)   Convert the top speed of the vehicle to metres per second.

          ii)   Calculate the maximum kinetic energy of the vehicle .

    b)   The engine is turned off when the vehicle is moving at its top speed and the vehicle coasts to a stop. The stopping distance is 25 m.

       Calculate the average frictional force acting on the vehicle.

19. A trolley of mass 3.0 kg accelerates from rest to 8.0 m s^{-1} in 12 s.
It continues at this speed for 8.0 s, before decelerating to rest in 5.0 s.

    a)   Draw the speed-time graph for the motion of the trolley.

    b)   i)   Calculate the total distance travelled by the trolley.

          ii)   Calculate the initial force acting on the trolley.

          iii) Calculate the braking force.

20. A truck of mass 16 000 kg is accelerating at 3.2 m s^{-2}.
The frictional force acting on the truck is 2750 N.

    Calculate the engine force of the truck.

21. A rocket in space has a mass of 6000 kg and accelerates at 6.0 m s^{-2}.
A short time later, a section of the rocket is detached and the mass decreases to 2400 kg, although the engine force remains constant.

    Calculate the new acceleration of the rocket.

22. A trolley, mass 2.5 kg, is accelerated from rest by a constant resultant force of 1.25 N.
After 8.0 s the applied force is removed and the trolley slows down and stops after a further 2.0 s. The frictional force is constant.

    a)   i)   Calculate the initial acceleration of the trolley.

          ii)   Calculate the speed of the trolley after 8.0 s.

    b)   i)   Calculate the deceleration of the trolley.

          ii)   Calculate the frictional force acting on the trolley.

          iii) What was the size of the applied force during the initial acceleration?

23. A box, mass 800 g, is lifted vertically from rest.
The box moves at a speed of 1.2 m s^{-1} after 5.0 s.

    Calculate the minimum force that must be applied.

24. A van and driver have a total mass of 1700 kg. The maximum acceleration of the vehicle with the driver is 3.4 m s^{-2}.
The van picks up four passengers, plus their luggage. The passengers have an average mass of 70 kg. With the same engine force, the van with the occupants and luggage has a maximum acceleration of 2.8 m s^{-2}.

a) Calculate the engine force required to reach maximum acceleration of the van with the driver alone.

b) i) What is the total mass of the four passengers?

ii) Calculate the mass of the luggage.

25. A rocket has a mass of 5.0 x 10^4 kg and initially accelerates from Earth at 9.0 m s^{-2}.

a) What is the weight of the rocket?

b) Calculate the minimum engine force that is applied to accelerate the rocket.

26. A 2.0 kg trolley is pulled from rest by a 15 N force for 7.0 s.
At this point the force is removed.
There is a frictional force of 6.0 N acting on the trolley.

a) i) Calculate the initial acceleration of the trolley.

ii) Calculate the speed of the trolley after 7.0 s.

b) Calculate the time taken by the trolley to come to rest, after the 15 N force is removed.

c) i) Draw the speed-time graph for the motion of the trolley.

ii) Calculate the total distance travelled by the trolley.

27. A sky-diver jumps out of an aeroplane and falls towards Earth.
As he accelerates due to gravity, friction increases.
After 9.0 s, he begins to fall at a constant velocity of 54 ms^{-1}.
After another 7.0 s, he opens his parachute and his downward speed decreases.
Eventually, after another 6.0 s, he reaches a new lower constant speed of 10 ms^{-1} , before finally hitting the ground 30 s after leaving the plane.

Draw a speed-time graph for the motion of the sky-diver
(numbers required on both axes).

Projectile motion

For the questions in this section, assume that air resistance can be ignored.

1. A ball is kicked off the top of a cliff and lands 26 m from the bottom of the cliff 4.0 s later.

   a) Calculate the horizontal speed of the ball.

   b) Calculate the vertical speed of the ball just before it reaches point **X**.

   c) Draw a velocity-time graph (numbers required on both axes) to represent:

      i) the horizontal motion;

      ii) the vertical motion.

   d) Calculate the height of the cliff.

2. A ball travelling at 3.2 m s^{-1} rolls off a table and lands on the floor 0.50 s later.

   a) Calculate the horizontal distance from the edge of the table to the landing point.

   b) Calculate the vertical speed of the ball just before it hits the floor.

   c) Draw a velocity-time graph (numbers required on both axes) to represent:

      i) the horizontal motion;

      ii) the vertical motion.

   d) Calculate the height of the table.

3. An aid aircraft, flying in level flight at a speed of 240 m s^{-1}, drops a food parcel. The parcel lands on the ground 11 s later.

   a) Calculate the vertical speed of the parcel just before it hits the ground.

   b) Draw a velocity-time graph (numbers required on both axes) to represent:

      i) the horizontal motion;

      ii) the vertical motion.

   c) Calculate the height of the aircraft above the ground.

   d) Calculate the horizontal displacement of the parcel from the point it leaves the aircraft.

4. A coin is thrown horizontally at 2.8 m s⁻¹, from the top of a tower and lands on the ground 8.0 s later.

   a) Calculate the horizontal distance from the top of the tower to where the coin hits the ground.

   b) Calculate the final vertical speed of the coin.

   c) Calculate the height of the tower.

5. A package is dropped from a helicopter that is moving with a horizontal speed of 48 m s⁻¹. The package travels 432 m horizontally as it falls from the helicopter, before hitting the ground.

   a) Calculate the vertical speed of the package just before it hits the ground.

   b) Calculate the height of the helicopter above the ground when the package is dropped.

6. A package is dropped from an aircraft that is moving with a horizontal speed of 84 m s⁻¹.
The package travels 840 m horizontally as it falls from the aircraft , before hitting the ground.

   a) i) What is the initial vertical speed of the package?

      ii) What is the vertical acceleration of the package?

   b) Calculate the time taken for the package to hit the ground.

   c) Calculate the vertical speed of the package just before it hits the ground.

   d) Draw a velocity-time graph (numbers required on both axes) to represent:

      i) the horizontal motion;

      ii) the vertical motion.

   e) Calculate the height of the aircraft above the ground when the package is dropped.

7. A diver takes a running dive off a vertical cliff and is in the air for 1.5 s before going into the water. The diver enters the water 1.2 m from the bottom of the cliff.

a) Calculate the horizontal speed of the diver.

b) Calculate the vertical speed of the diver on entering the water.

c) Draw a velocity-time graph (numbers required on both axes) to represent:

i) the horizontal motion;

ii) the vertical motion.

d) Calculate the height of the cliff.

8. A ball is kicked horizontally from a vertical cliff at 8.0 m s⁻¹ and lands on the ground 36 m from the bottom of the cliff.

a) Calculate the time the ball is in the air.

b) Calculate the vertical speed of the ball just before it hits the ground.

c) Calculate the height of the cliff.

SPACE

Space travel and exploration

1. A space station orbits 200 km above the Earth.
    The gravitational field strength is 7.0 N kg^{-1} at this height.
    An astronaut has a mass of 62 kg.

    Calculate the weight of the astronaut at this height.

2. A pulse of laser light is sent from NASA to reflect off a mirror placed on the Moon. The pulse is received back at NASA 1.28 s later.

    Calculate the distance between the Earth and the Moon.

3. It takes 500 s for light to travel to Earth from the Sun.

    Calculate the distance between the Earth and the Sun.

4. The distance between Earth and Mars is 115 million kilometres.

    a) A spacecraft takes 250 days to travel this distance.

        Calculate the average speed of the spacecraft, in metres per second.

    b) A radio signal is sent to the spacecraft on Mars.

        Calculate the time taken for the signal to arrive.

5. A satellite is in a geostationary orbit at 36 000 km above a ground station.

    Calculate the time taken for a microwave signal to travel to the satellite and back to the ground station.

6. A meteorite, mass 35 kg, enters the atmosphere at 15 km s^{-1}.
    It is slowed by friction in the atmosphere to 85 m s^{-1} in a distance of 30 km.

    Calculate the kinetic energy of the meteorite:

    a) as it enters the atmosphere;

    b) after it has been slowed by friction in the atmosphere.

7. A satellite has a mass of 480 kg and is travelling at 8300 m s^{-1}.
    It needs to slow down to 7600 m s^{-1}, in the same direction, in order to move into the correct orbit.

    Calculate the change in kinetic energy required.

8. A rocket of mass 2260 kg is travelling at 1600 m s^{-1} when the second stage engine ignites. This engine accelerates the rocket to 8600 m s^{-1} over the next 35 s.

   a) Calculate the change in kinetic energy.

   b) i) Calculate the average acceleration.

      ii) Calculate the average force causing this acceleration.

   c) The rocket is still close to Earth, moving vertically, when the acceleration occurs.

      Calculate the force provided by the second stage engine.

9. An unmanned space-craft, mass 980 kg, is used to remove waste from a space station. The craft is disposable and after leaving the Space Station it vaporises in the atmosphere along with the waste.

   Calculate the energy required to vaporise the space-craft and its contents At its boiling point when the craft is carrying 700 kg waste.

   (Assume that all materials that make up the space-craft and its contents are at their boiling point. Take the average latent heat of vaporisation to be 8.5 x 10^6 J kg^{-1}.)

10. A spacecraft is powered by large wings that carry a total of 480 photocells. At the height of the spacecraft, each of the photocells produce a voltage of 2.6 V with a current of 65 mA.

    Calculate the power that can be produced by the total number of photocells on a wing.

11. A 400 g sample of a meteorite is tested to find the specific latent heat of fusion of the material. The sample is heated to the melting point and then is melted using a 2.5 kW heating system. This takes 48 s.

    Use this data to calculate the specific latent heat of fusion of the material.

12. A geostationary satellite orbits at a height of 36 000 km.
    A polar orbiting satellite takes 100 minutes to complete one orbit.

    a) What is the time for one complete orbit for the geostationary satellite?

    b) Give an approximate height for the polar satellite.

13. A space capsule with a mass of 1780 kg re-enters the Earth's atmosphere at 2600 m s^{-1}.

    a) Calculate the kinetic energy of the capsule.

    b) Calculate the maximum increase in temperature of the capsule.

    (Take the average specific heat capacity to be 970 J kg^{-1} $^\circ$C^{-1}.)

For questions 14 and 15, use information from the tables shown on the Data Sheet on pages i and ii.

14. A spacecraft of mass 3750 kg is on the Moon.
    The engine force of the craft on take-off is 60 kN.
    The spacecraft reaches an escape speed of 4500 m s^{-1} on leaving the Moon.

    a) Calculate the weight of the spacecraft on the Moon.

    b) i) Calculate the acceleration of the spacecraft.

       ii) Calculate the time that it takes for the escape speed to be reached.

15. An iron meteoroid has a mass of 85 g and is travelling at 7200 m s^{-1} when it hits the Earth's atmosphere.
    The temperature of the meteoroid on entering the atmosphere is -10 $^\circ$C.

    a) Calculate the kinetic energy of the meteor.

    b) i) Calculate the energy needed to raise the temperature of the meteoroid to its melting point.

       ii) Calculate the energy needed to melt the meteoroid.

Light years

1. Light from the far side of our Galaxy takes 100 000 years to reach Earth.

   a) Calculate the number of metres in one light year.

   b) What is the distance between Earth and the far side of our Galaxy?

2. The Sun is 1.5×10^8 km from Earth.

   Calculate the time taken for infra-red rays to reach the Earth from the Sun.

3. A radio signal from a space-craft takes 5 hours 20 minutes to reach Earth.

   Calculate the distance, in metres, between the Earth and the space-craft.

4. The nearest star other than the Sun is Proxima Centauri.
   Light from this star takes 4.3 years to reach the Earth.

   a) i) What is the distance between Earth and Proxima Centauri, in light years?

   ii) Calculate the distance between Earth and Proxima Centauri, in metres.

   b) The Voyager spacecraft travels at approximately 17.3 km s^{-1}.

   Calculate the time in years that it would take for Voyager to reach Proxima Centauri.

5. Canis Major is a dwarf galaxy about 42 000 light years from Earth.

   Calculate the distance between Earth and Canis Major, in metres.

ELECTRICTY

Electrical current and voltage

1. In each of the following circuits, state the unknown value:

    a) for the currents I_1 to I_6;

    b) for the voltages V_1 to V_4.

    i)

    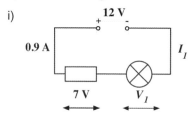

    ii)

    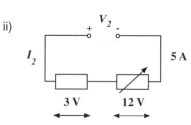

    iii)

    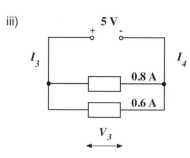

    iv)

    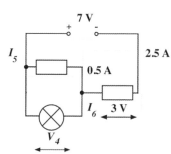

2. In each of the following circuits, state the unknown value:

    a) for the currents I_1 to I_6;

    b) for the voltages V_1 to V_4.

    i)

    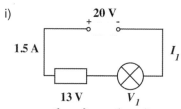

    ii)

    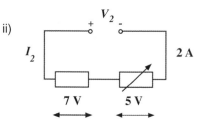

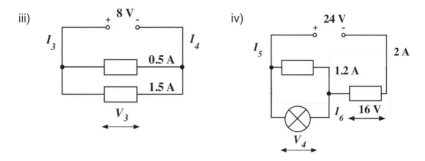

3.

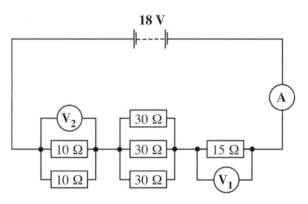

The reading on the ammeter is 0.6 A; the reading on voltmeter V_1 is 9 V; the reading on voltmeter V_2 is 3 V.

a)   What is the voltage across the 30 Ω resistors?

b)   State the current:

   i)   in the 15 Ω resistor;

   ii)   in each of the 30 Ω resistors;

   iii)   in each of the 10 Ω resistors.

Series and parallel circuits

1. State the formula that is used to calculate the total resistance R_T, of three resistors R_1, R_2 and R_3:

    a) when connected in series;

    b) when connected in parallel.

2. Calculate the total resistance between points **X** and **Y** for each of the following combinations of resistors.

    a)

    O—[6 Ω]—[18 Ω]—O
    X   **Y**

    b)

    O—[0.6 kΩ]—[1.4 kΩ]—O
    X   **Y**

    c)

    O—[1.6 kΩ]—[150 Ω]—O
    X   **Y**

3. Calculate the total resistance between points **X** and **Y** for each of the following combinations of resistors.

    a)

    ```
         [ 6 Ω ]
    O—●          ●—O
    X   [ 6 Ω ]   Y
    ```

    b)

    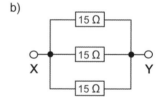

    c)

    ```
      [ 6 Ω ]
      [ 6 Ω ]
      [ 6 Ω ]
    O—
    X [ 6 Ω ] Y
      [ 6 Ω ]
      [ 6 Ω ]
    ```

    d)

    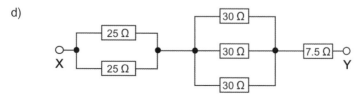

4. Calculate the total resistance between points **X** and **Y** for each of the following combinations of resistors.

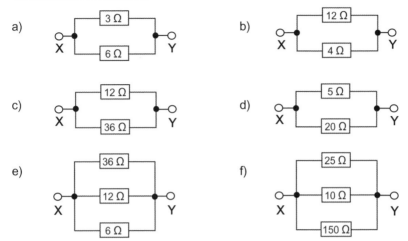

a) 3 Ω, 6 Ω

b) 12 Ω, 4 Ω

c) 12 Ω, 36 Ω

d) 5 Ω, 20 Ω

e) 36 Ω, 12 Ω, 6 Ω

f) 25 Ω, 10 Ω, 150 Ω

5. Calculate the total resistance between points **X** and **Y** for each of the following combinations of resistors.

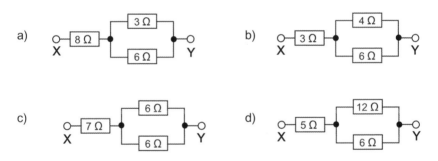

a) 8 Ω, 3 Ω, 6 Ω

b) 3 Ω, 4 Ω, 6 Ω

c) 7 Ω, 6 Ω, 6 Ω

d) 5 Ω, 12 Ω, 6 Ω

6. Calculate the total resistance of ten 50 Ω resistors:

a) when connected in series;

b) when connected in parallel.

7. Calculate the total resistance between points **X** and **Y** for each of the following combinations of resistors.

a) 20 Ω, 20 Ω, 80 Ω

b) 10 Ω, 10 Ω, 80 Ω

8. The same three resistors are connected in four different ways as shown. In each case, calculate the total resistance between points **X** and **Y**.

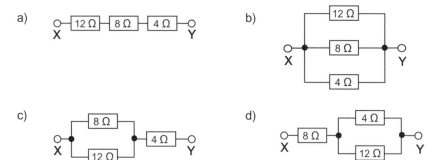

a)

b)

c)

d)

9. Calculate the total resistance of the circuit shown.

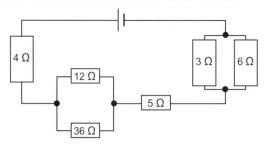

10. Draw a circuit that uses five resistors of resistance 3 Ω, 6 Ω, 10 Ω, 10 Ω and 15 Ω to give a total resistance of 22 Ω.

11. Draw a circuit that uses five resistors of resistance 6 Ω, 6 Ω, 12 Ω, 15 Ω and 30 Ω to give a total resistance of 20 Ω.

12. Four resistors R_1 to R_4 have a resistance of 1 Ω, 10 Ω, 100 Ω, and 1000 Ω respectively.

    a) What is the approximate total resistance when they are connected in series?

    b) What is the approximate total resistance when they are connected in parallel?

    For each part of the question, choose from:
    A less than 1 Ω;
    B between 1 Ω and 10 Ω;
    C between 10 Ω and 100 Ω;
    D between 100 Ω and 1000 Ω;
    E greater than 1000 Ω.

Ohm's Law

1. Rewrite each of the following voltages (potential differences).
    a) 0.75 V in millivolts.
    b) 3.2 V in millivolts.
    c) 870 mV in volts.
    d) 2963 mV in volts.
    e) 250 μV in volts.
    f) 0.04 V in microvolts.

2. Rewrite each of the following currents.
    a) 120 A in milliamps.
    b) 0.03 A in milliamps.
    c) 5805 mA in amps.
    d) 2 mA in amps.
    e) 756 μA in amps.
    f) 8.9 A in microamps.

3. a) State the equation that links **voltage** with **current** and **resistance**.
    b) State the symbol for each quantity.
    b) State the unit for each quantity, and its abbreviation.

4. A relationship exists between the voltage V across a resistor and the current I in it.
    a) In what way does the ratio $\frac{V}{I}$ vary as the voltage across the resistor is increased?
    b) In what way does the current vary as the voltage across the resistor is increased?

5. Calculate the resistance of each of the following.
    a) A lamp with a current of 3.0 A in it when connected to a 24 V battery.
    b) A resistor with a current of 6.0 A in it when connected to a 230 V supply.
    c) A resistor with a current of 30 mA in it when connected to a 6.0 V supply.

6. Calculate the current in each of the following.

    a) A 220 Ω resistor connected across a 5.0 V supply.

    b) A 2.0 kΩ resistor connected across a 9.0 V battery.

    c) A 12 V transformer connected to a circuit of resistance 1.2 kΩ.

7. Calculate the voltage required to produce each of the following.

    a) A current of 0.50 A in a 30 Ω resistor.

    b) A current of 3.0 mA in a 500 Ω resistor.

    c) A current of 5.0 mA in a 1.5 kΩ resistor.

8. A power supply of 24 kV produces a current in a circuit of 1.6 mA. Calculate the resistance of the circuit.

9. A 10 kΩ resistor is connected across a 12 V power supply. Calculate the current in the resistor.

10. A current of 3.5 mA is measured in a 10 kΩ resistor. Calculate the voltage across the resistor.

11. In a series circuit, ammeter readings are taken in turn with each of four different resistors, R_1 to R_4, in the circuit.
    The four ammeter readings are: 0.064 A, 40 mA, 3.2 A, 10.7 mA.
    The supply voltage across each of the resistors kept constant.

    a) Copy and complete the table below, placing the ammeter readings, in the correct row.

Resistor	Resistance (Ω)	Current
R_1	5	
R_2	250	
R_3	400	
R_4	1.5 k	

    b) Calculate the voltage of the supply.

12. In each of the following circuits, calculate the unknown value for R_1, I_1, V_1 and R_2.

a)

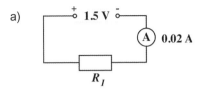

b)

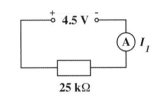

c)

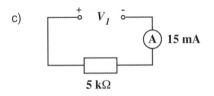

d)

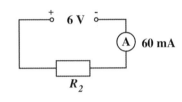

13. A circuit is set up as shown.
    The lamp is rated at 6V, 60 mA.

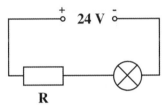

   a) i) What is the voltage across the resistor when the lamp is operating at its rated value?

   ii) What is the current in the resistor?

   b) Calculate the resistance of resistor R.

14. Calculate the resistance of resistor R in each of the following circuits. Each lamp is operating at its rated value.

a)

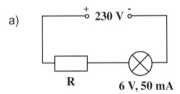

b)

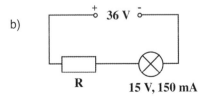

15. a) Calculate the total resistance in the circuit.

    b) Calculate the current supplied by the battery.

    c) What is the current in the 4 Ω resistor?

    d) Calculate the voltage:

        i)   across the 4 Ω resistor;

        ii) across the parallel network.

    e) Calculate the current:

        i)   in the 3 Ω resistor;

        ii) in the 6 Ω resistor.

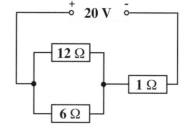

16. a) Calculate the current supplied by the battery.

    b) Calculate the current:

        i)   in the 6 Ω resistor;

        ii) in the 12 Ω resistor.

17.

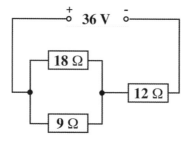

Calculate the current:

a)   in the 12 Ω resistor;

b)   in the 9 Ω resistor;

c)   in the 18 Ω resistor.

18.

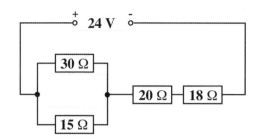

a) i) Calculate the current in the 18 Ω resistor.

   ii) What is the current in the 20 Ω resistor?

b) Calculate the current:

   i) in the 15 Ω resistor;

   ii) in the 30 Ω resistor.

19.

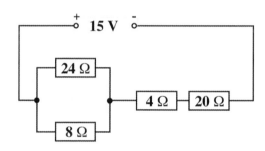

Calculate the current:

a) in the 24 Ω resistor;

b) in the 8 Ω resistor.

Potential dividers

1. Calculate the voltages V_1 and V_2 for each of the following circuits.

a)

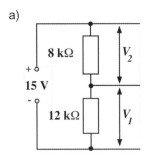

b)

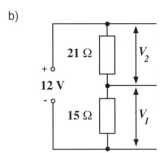

c)

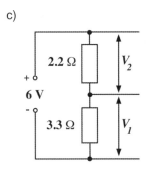

d)

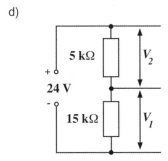

e)

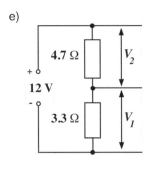

f)

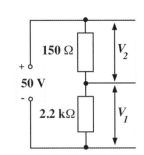

2. Calculate the voltage V_1 and resistance R_1 for each of the following circuits.

a)

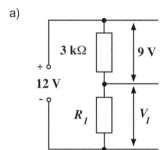

b)

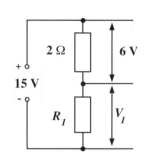

c)

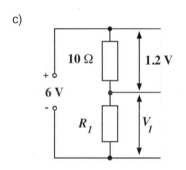

d)

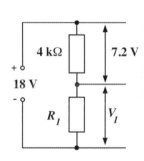

e)

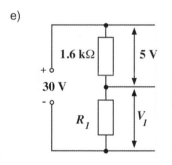

f)

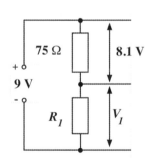

3. The diagram shows a potentiometer. **X** is a variable contact, that can move from point **A** at the bottom of the resistor to point **B** at the top.

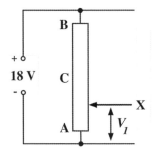

Calculate the voltage V_1:

a) when contact **X** is at point **A**;

b) when contact **X** is at point **B**;

c) when contact **X** is at point **C**, the midpoint.

4. A 20 kΩ potentiometer **AB** is connected across a 6 V d.c. power supply as shown.

The sliding contact, **P**, can be moved to any point along the potentiometer.

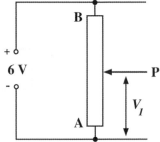

a) State the output voltage V_1:

   i) when sliding contact **P** is at point **A**;

   ii) when sliding contact **P** is at point **B**;

   iii) when sliding contact **P** is midway between **A** and **B**;

   iv) when sliding contact **P** is one third of the way along the length of the potentiometer from point **A**.

b) The potentiometer is adjusted so that the output voltage V_1, is 4.5 V.

   Calculate the resistance between point **A** and the position of the sliding contact **P**.

5. a) Calculate the output voltage V_1 in circuit 1.

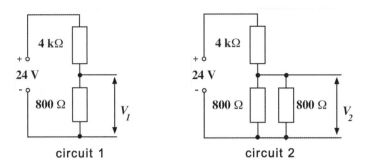

circuit 1   circuit 2

b) A second identical 800 Ω resistor is connected across points **XY** as shown in circuit 2.

Calculate the new output voltage V_2.

6. Calculate the voltage V_1 and resistance R_1 for each of the following circuits.

a)   b)   c)

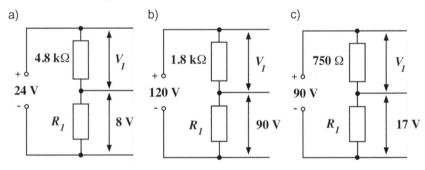

7. A power supply has a fixed output voltage of 6 V.
A potential divider is to be used with this supply to provide a constant voltage of 1.5 V.

Design a potential divider circuit that will give this constant voltage.

All resistors used must have whole number values.

8. A 240 V d.c. power supply is to be used with a potential divider to produce an output voltage of 20 V.

Design a potential divider circuit that will give this constant output.

All resistors used must have whole number values.

Electric charge and electrical current

1. a) State the equation that links **electric charge** with **electrical current** and **time**.

   b) State the symbol for each quantity.

   c) State the unit for each quantity, and its abbreviation.

2. Calculate the total charge through each of the following.

   a) A heater having a current of 8.0 A for 30 s.

   b) A lamp having a current of 1.5 A for 1 minute.

   c) A resistor having a current of 500 mA for 5 minutes.

3. Calculate the current in each of the following.

   a) When 150 C of charge pass through a lamp filament in 200 s.

   b) When 3600 C of charge pass through a switch in 5 minutes.

   c) When 15 000 C of charge pass through a circuit in 10 minutes.

4. Calculate the time taken for each of the following.

   a) A current of 5.0 A to pass 400 C of charge through a resistor.

   b) A current of 200 mA to pass 10 C of charge through a headlamp

   c) A current of 20 mA to pass 5 C of charge through a circuit.

5. A charge of 600 C pass through a lamp for 3 minutes.

   Calculate the current in the lamp.

6. A car battery stores 5.25×10^4 C of charge.

   Calculate the time for which a current of 2.5 A can be supplied by the battery.

7. The current in a circuit is 350 mA.

   Calculate the charge that is transferred in 2 hours.

For questions 8 to 10, take the charge on a single electron to be 1.6×10^{-19} C.

8. a) Calculate the charge that is transferred from a battery when a current of 50 A flows for 30 s.

   b) Calculate the number of electrons that are transferred.

9. a) Calculate the charge that is transferred when a current of 80 mA flows for 15 minutes.

   b) Calculate the number of electrons that are transferred.

10. An adaptor is plugged into a socket to allow a lamp, a laptop and a television to operate at the same time. There is a current of 0.26 A in the lamp, 1.3 A in the laptop and 2.6 A in the television.

    a) What is the total current in the socket?

    b) Calculate the charge transferred through the socket when all three appliances are on for 50 minutes.

    c) Calculate the number of electrons that are transferred.

Electrical power and energy

1. a) State the equation that links **electrical power** with **energy** and **time**.

   b) State the symbol for each quantity.

   b) State the unit for each quantity, and its abbreviation.

2. State the electrical energy that is transformed in one second by each of the following:

   a) A 60 W lamp.

   b) A 5 kW heater.

   c) A 20 mW electronic component.

3. Calculate the power rating of each of the following.

   a) A motor that transforms 1200 J in 20 s.

   b) A heater that transforms 2.4 MJ in 20 minutes.

   c) A soldering iron that transforms120 kJ in 5 minutes.

4. Calculate the electrical energy that is transformed by each of the following.

   a) A 600 W drill in use for 75 s.

   b) An 800 W iron in use for 45 minutes.

   c) A 2.3 kW kettle in use for 5 minutes.

5. Calculate the time that it takes for each of the following.

   a) A 3000 W heater to use 900 kJ of energy.

   b) A 100 W lamp to use 600 kJ of energy.

   c) A 2 kW kettle to use 120 kJ of energy.

6. A small electrical component is rated at 15 mW.

   Calculate the energy that it uses in 10 minutes.

7. Calculate the power rating of a motor that uses 2.4 MJ in 40 minutes.

8. Calculate the time that it takes for a 750 W drill to use 630 kJ of energy.

9. A coal power station burns enough coal to give 1440 MW of power each day. Some of the power is lost in generating the electricity. As a result, the station only gives 500 MW to the National Grid each day.

a) Calculate the energy that is given by the power station to the grid each day.

b) i) Calculate the energy that is given by the coal each day.

ii) Calculate the mass of coal that is used each day.

(Assume that 1 kg of coal gives 37.2 MJ of energy.)

Electrical power, current and voltage

1. a) State the equation that links **electrical power** with **current** and **voltage**.

    b) State the symbol for each quantity.

    b) State the unit for each quantity, and its abbreviation.

2. Calculate the power of each of the following appliances.

    a) A vacuum cleaner that is connected to the 230 V mains supply and requires a current of 3.0 A.

    b) A personal stereo that is connected to a 9.0 V battery and requires a current of 25 mA.

    c) A motor that is connected to the 230 V mains supply and requires a current of 13 A.

3. Calculate the current required for the following appliances.

    a) A heater rated at 1.5 kW that is connected to the 230 V mains supply.

    b) A 6.0 V toy car rated at 25 mW.

    c) An industrial motor requiring a 1500 V supply and rated at 45 kW.

4. Calculate the voltage required for each of the following appliances.

    a) A 30 W lamp when the current in it is 2.5 A.

    b) A 2.5 kW kettle when the current in it is 10 A.

    c) A 7.5 mW diode when the current in it is 2500 µA.

5. Calculate the voltage across electricity cables when the current is 1500 A and the power is 6.75 MW.

6. Calculate the power of a 12 V toy train when the current in it is 0.80 A.

7. Calculate the current in a 3.0 kW kettle that is connected to the 230 V mains supply.

Electrical power, current and resistance

1. a) State the equation that links **electrical power** with **current** and **resistance**.

   b) State the symbol for each quantity.

   b) State the unit for each quantity, and its abbreviation.

2. Calculate the power dissipated in each of the following.

   a) A 5.0 Ω resistor when the current in it is 4.0 A.

   b) A 4.7 MΩ resistor when the current in it is 75 μA.

   c) A 3.0 x 10⁴ Ω resistor when the current in it is 15 A.

   d) A 220 Ω resistor when the current in it is 45 mA.

3. Calculate the resistance of each of the following resistors operating at its rated value.

   a) A resistor that has a power rating of 60 W when the current is 2.0 A.

   b) A resistor that has a power rating of 150 W when the current is 5.0 A.

   c) A resistor that has a power rating of 3.0 mW when the current is 6.0 μA.

   d) A resistor that has a power rating of 7.0 MW when the current is 75 A.

4. Calculate the current in each of the following resistors operating at its rated value.

   a) A 100 Ω resistor with a power rating of 4.0 W.

   b) A 50 Ω resistor, with a power rating of 2.0 kW.

   c) A 30 kΩ resistor with a power rating of 5.0 MW.

   d) A 470 Ω resistor with a power rating of 35 kW.

5. Calculate the power rating in each of the following devices in a car.

   a) A radio of resistance 12 Ω with a current of 20 mA.

   b) The rear window heater of resistance 3.0 Ω with a current of 4.0 A.

6. Calculate the resistance of a hairdryer element that has a power rating of 960 W when the current in it is 4.0 A.

7. Calculate the current in a 25 kΩ resistor when it is used at its rated value of 650 kW.

Electrical power, voltage and resistance

1. a) State the equation that links **electrical power** with **voltage** and **resistance**.

   b) State the symbol for each quantity.

   c) State the unit for each quantity, and its abbreviation.

2. Calculate the power dissipated in each of the following.

   a) A 5.0 Ω resistor with a voltage of 20 V across it.

   b) A 4.5 x 10³ Ω resistor connected across a 230 V supply.

   c) A 6.8 Ω resistor when the voltage across it is 25 mV.

3. Calculate the resistance of each of the following.

   a) A resistor that dissipates a power of 30 W when connected to a 12 V supply.

   b) A resistor that dissipates a power of 2.5 kW when connected to a 230 V supply.

   c) A resistor that dissipates a power of 3 MW when connected to a 1.5 kV supply.

4. Calculate the voltage that can be connected across each of the following when the resistor is operating at its rated value:

   a) A 50 Ω resistor with a power rating of 200 W.

   b) A 75 Ω resistor with a power rating of 70 W.

   c) A 6.5 kΩ resistor with a power rating of 8.5 W.

5. A resistor is connected across a 12 V supply.
   The power dissipated is 40 W.

   Calculate the resistance of the resistor.

6. Calculate the power rating for a mains heater with a resistance of 1.5 x 10³ Ω.

7. A 7.5 kΩ resistor has a power rating of 12 W.

   Calculate the voltage that can be connected across it.

Mixed electricity problems (i)

1. The current in a 9.0 V lamp is 800 mA.

   a) Calculate the power rating of the lamp.

   b) Calculate the energy that would be used by the lamp in 1 hour.

2. In 5 minutes a charge of 1500 C flows through a resistor that dissipates a power of 70 W.

   a) Calculate the current in the resistor.

   b) Calculate the resistance of the resistor.

3. A circuit is set up as shown.
   Each lamp is operating at its rated value.

   a) Calculate the current :

      i)   in lamp A;

      ii) in lamp B.

   b) Calculate the resistance:

      i)   of lamp A;

      ii) of lamp B.

   c) Calculate the total energy that is transferred to the **two** lamps in15 minutes.

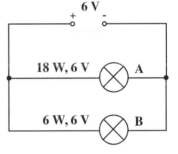

4. A laptop rated at 350 W, a television rated at 85 W and a kettle rated at 2 kW, are all connected to the mains supply (230 V).
   The three appliances are switched on.

   a) Calculate the current:

      i)   in the laptop;

      ii)   in the television;

      iii) in the kettle.

   b) i) What is the total power dissipated in the **three** appliances?

      ii) Calculate the total energy used by the three appliances when they are all switched on for 3 minutes 45 s.

5. A circuit is set up as shown.
   Each lamp is operating at its rated value.

   a) Calculate the current:
      i) in lamp **A**;
      ii) in lamp **B**.
   b) Calculate the resistance:
      i) of lamp **A**;
      ii) of lamp **B**.
   c) i) What is the current in resistor **R**?
      ii) What is the voltage across resistor **R**?
   d) Calculate the resistance of resistor **R**.

6. A mains heater supplies 16.2 MJ of energy in 90 minutes.
   a) Calculate the power of the heater.
   b) Calculate the resistance of the heater.
   c) Calculate the current in the heater.

7. There is a current of 0.196 A in a television when it is connected to the 230 V mains supply. When left on, the television transforms 5640 J of energy.
   Calculate the time for which the television is on.

8. A mains appliance uses 9.75 MJ of energy in 25 minutes.
   a) Calculate the power of the appliance.
   b) Calculate the current in the appliance.
   c) Calculate the resistance of the appliance.

9. An electrical appliance uses a 12 V battery.
   In 2.5 hours it uses 8.1×10^4 J of energy.
   a) Calculate the power of the appliance.
   b) Calculate the resistance of the appliance.
   c) Calculate the current in the appliance.
   d) Calculate the charge that is transferred in the 2.5 hours.

10. a) Calculate the power rating for a mains heater (230 V) with a resistance of 8.0 Ω.

b) Calculate the total energy transferred when it is switched on for 2.5 hours.

11. a) Calculate the resistance of a 750 W travel kettle when it is connected to a 12.0 V battery.

b) An energy of 280 kJ is required to boil water in a kettle.

Calculate the time taken to boil the water.

12. A mains appliance (230 V) has a resistance of 18.0 Ω.

a) Calculate the power of the appliance.

b) Calculate the current in the appliance.

13. An appliance is rated at 12.5 A, 7.5 Ω.

a) Calculate the power of the appliance.

b) Calculate the supply voltage required by the appliance.

c) Calculate the energy used in 1 hour.

d) Calculate the charge transferred in 1 hour.

Mixed electricity problems (ii)

1. A cycle lamp has a resistance of 4.0 Ω and runs off a 3.0 V battery.
    The battery can supply a total charge of 7200 C.
    a) Calculate the current in the lamp.
    b) Calculate the charge passing through the lamp in 10 minutes.
    c) Calculate the time for which the lamp can stay on.

2. Three resistors of resistance 50 Ω, 300 Ω and 600 Ω are connected in series.
    The current in the circuit is 8.0 mA.
    a) i) Calculate the voltage across each resistor.
        ii) What is the supply voltage across the series combination?
    b) i) Calculate the power dissipated in each resistor.
        ii) What is the total power dissipated in the circuit?
    c) Calculate the total energy used in the circuit in 5 minutes.
    d) Calculate the total charge transferred in 5 minutes.

3. Three resistors of resistance 50 Ω, 300 Ω and 600 Ω are connected in
    parallel. The supply voltage for the circuit is 36 V.
    a) i) Calculate the current in each resistor.
        ii) What is the total current in the circuit?
    b) i) Calculate the power dissipated in each resistor.
        ii) What is the total power dissipated in the circuit?
    c) Calculate the total energy used in the circuit in 5 minutes.
    d) Calculate the total charge transferred from the battery in 5 minutes.

4. A low voltage heater is controlled by a
    variable resistor.

    The variable resistor is adjusted to a
    resistance of 50 Ω and the potential
    difference across the heater, V_1, is 2.8 V.

    a) What is the potential difference V_2
        across the variable resistor?
    b) Calculate the resistance of the heater.
    c) Calculate the current in the circuit.
    d) Calculate the power dissipated by the heater.

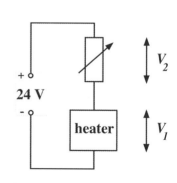

5. A circuit is set up as shown. All the lamps are identically rated at 36 W, 12 V and working at their rated value.

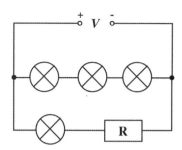

a) What is the supply voltage V that is required?
b) Calculate the resistance of one lamp.
c) What is the resistance of resistor R, required to ensure that all lamps are working at their rated value?
d) Calculate the total resistance of the circuit.
e) Calculate the total current in the circuit.

6.

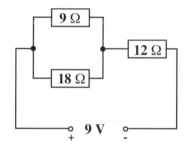

a) i)   Calculate the current in the 12 Ω resistor.
    ii)   Calculate the voltage across the 12 Ω resistor.
    iii) Calculate the power of the 12 Ω resistor.
b) i)   Calculate the current in the 9 Ω resistor.
    ii)   Calculate the voltage across the 9 Ω resistor.
    iii) Calculate the power of the 9 Ω resistor.
c) i)   Calculate the current in the 18 Ω resistor.
    ii)   Calculate the voltage across the 18 Ω resistor.
    iii) Calculate the power of the 18 Ω resistor.

7.

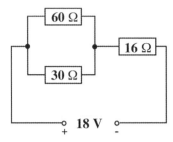

a) i) Calculate the current in the 16 Ω resistor.

ii) Calculate the voltage across the 16 Ω resistor.

iii) Calculate the power of the 16 Ω resistor.

b) i) Calculate the current in the 30 Ω resistor.

ii) Calculate the voltage across the 30 Ω resistor.

iii) Calculate the power of the 30 Ω resistor.

c) i) Calculate the current in the 60 Ω resistor.

ii) Calculate the voltage across the 60 Ω resistor.

iii) Calculate the power of the 60 Ω resistor.

8. In the two circuits, **A** and **B**, all the lamps are identical and rated at 12 V, 2 A.

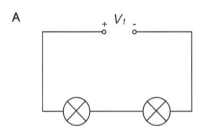
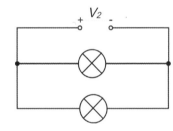

The lamps are required to operate at normal brightness (rated voltage and current).

a) State the supply voltage:

i) V_1 that is required for circuit **A**;

ii) V_2 that is required for circuit **B**.

b) i) Show that the resistance of each bulb used in these circuits is 6 Ω.

ii) Calculate the total resistance of circuit **B**.

c) Calculate the total power that is dissipated:

i) in circuit **A**;

ii) in circuit **B**.

Fuses

For each of the following domestic appliances, choose the correct rating for the fuse from the choice of 3 A or 13 A.

1. A 60 W lamp.

2. A 3 kW kettle.

3. A 750 W microwave.

4. A 9 kW cooker.

5. A 1200 W iron.

6. A 275 W television.

Domestic electricity

1. The kilowatt-hour (kWh) is the unit of electricity used in household electricity, e.g. a 3 kWh electric fire switched on for 2 hours uses 6 kWh.

    Calculate the number of kilowatt-hours that are used when:

    a) a 3.0 kW heater is switched on for 4 hours;

    b) a 350 W television is switched on for 2 hours 30 minutes;

    c) a 750 W microwave is switched on for 20 minutes

    d) five 40 W light bulbs are switched on for 8 hours 15 minutes

2. Calculate the total number of kilowatt hours that are used in each of the following appliances.

    a) A 5.0 kW heater, a 300 W television and three 60 W lamps all on for 2.5 hours.

    b) A 200 W computer, a 1200 W electric fan and a 350 W television all on for 4.5 hours.

    c) A 3.0 kW cooker on for 35 minutes and a 300 W television on for 1.5 hours.

    d) A 2.0 kW air conditioning unit on for 9 hours; a 250 W computer on for 4 hours 20 minutes and a 700 W microwave on for 12 minutes.

3. An electricity supplier charges £0.118 for each kilowatt-hour.

    Calculate the charge for running each of the following.

    a) A 7.0 kW cooker that is on for 1 hour 30 minutes.

    b) Five bulbs, each rated at 60 W that are on for 4 hours 20 minutes.

    c) A 75 W television that is on for 5 hours.

    d) A 3.0 kW kettle that is on for 20 minutes.

    e) A 350 W laptop that is on for 6 hours 25 minutes.

    f) A 2.5 kW heater that is on for 5 hours 45 minutes.

Electronics

1. The following data is given for a LED that is to be used with a 9.0 V supply.
    Maximum forward voltage: 2.3 V
    Maximum forward current: 55 mA

    Calculate the resistance of the resistor required to be connected in series that would allow the LED to operate at its maximum value.

2. Consider the following circuit.

    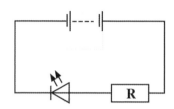

    The potential difference across the LED is 1.5 V and the battery voltage is 6.0 V. The current in the LED is 10 mA.

    Calculate the resistance of resistor R.

3. The operating data for the LED in the circuit is shown.

    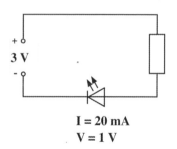

    $$I = 20 \ mA$$
    $$V = 1 \ V$$

    Calculate the resistance of the resistor that would allow the LED to work at its rated value.

4. Using the operating data given, calculate the resistance of the protective resistor required for each of the following LEDs to operate at its rated value.

    a) LED (V = 1.5 V   I = 20 mA), V_s = 6.0 V
    b) LED (V = 2.0 V   I = 10 mA), V_s = 10 V
    c) LED (V = 1.5 V   I = 25 mA), V_s = 5.0 V
    d) LED (V = 2.0 V   I = 20 mA), V_s = 12 V

5. An LED and resistor are connected in series to a 6 V supply as shown. The current through the LED is 20 mA at 2 V.

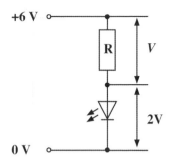

a) What is the voltage V across the resistor?

b) Calculate the resistance of resistor R.

6. When a thermistor is cold its resistance is 800 Ω.
It is connected in series with a 250 Ω resistor and the combination is connected across a 6.0 V supply

a) Calculate the voltage:

    i)   across the thermistor;

    ii)   across the resistor.

b) The thermistor is now placed in boiling water and its resistance changes to 150 Ω.

    Calculate the new voltage:

    i)   across the thermistor;

    ii)   across the resistor.

7. An LDR is connected to a 25 kΩ resistor as shown.
The values for its resistance in particular conditions are in the table.

Condition	Resistance
Sunlight	5 kΩ
Dark	100 kΩ

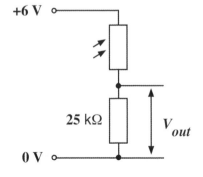

Calculate the output voltage V_{out}:

a) when the LDR is in the sunlight;

b) when the LDR is in the dark.

8. A thermistor is placed in a beaker of water and its resistance is measured at various temperatures. The following results are obtained:

Temperature (°C)	Resistance (Ω)
0	1000
10	720
20	540
30	?
40	365
50	300
60	250
70	205
80	165
100	100

a) i) Draw a graph of Resistance against Temperature.

ii) Use your graph to find the resistance of the thermistor at 30 °C.

b) The thermistor is connected to a 12 V battery.

Calculate the current in the thermistor when its temperature is 60 °C.

9. The resistance of an LDR is measured as the intensity of light on the LDR is varied. The following results are obtained:

Light intensity (units)	10	30	50	70	90	110
Resistance (kΩ)	500	285	190	?	95	65

a) i) Draw a graph of Resistance against Light Intensity.

ii) Use your graph to find the resistance of the LDR at 70 units of light intensity.

b) The LDR is connected to a 6.0 V battery.

Calculate the current in the LDR when the light intensity is 30 units.

10. An LDR of resistance 250 kΩ in darkness is placed in series with a 5.0 kΩ resistor. The supply voltage across the combination is 6.0 V d.c.

   a) Calculate the voltage:

   i) across the LDR;

   ii) across the resistor.

   b) The LDR is now placed in the light giving it a resistance of 12 kΩ. Calculate the new voltage:

   i) across the LDR;

   ii) across the resistor.

11. The resistance of the thermistor in the circuit is measured at different temperatures. The results are shown in the table.

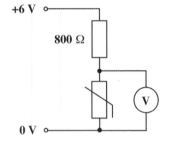

Temperature (ºC)	Resistance (Ω)
0	1100
30	800
60	400
100	200

   a) Calculate the reading on the voltmeter when the temperature of the thermistor is 30 °C.

   b) The thermistor is heated to 100 °C. Calculate the new reading on the voltmeter .

Switching circuits

1. A circuit is set up as shown. The npa transistor will switch on when a voltage V_{be} of 0.5 V is applied between the base and the emitter.

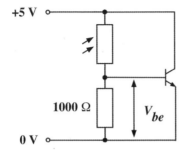

Calculate the resistance of the LDR that is required to turn on the transistor.

2. Consider the following potential divider circuit.

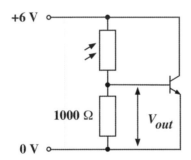

During a certain change in the environment, the resistance of the LDR changes from 9 kΩ to 1 kΩ.

Calculate the voltage V_{out}:

a) when the resistance of the LDR is 9 kΩ;

b) when the resistance of the LDR is 1 kΩ.

3. Consider the following circuit.

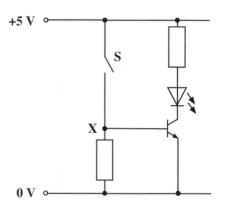

a) When switch **S** is open:
   i) state the potential at point **X**;
   ii) state whether the LED lit or unlit.

b) When switch **S** is closed:
   i) state the potential at point **X**;
   ii) state whether the LED is lit or unlit.

4. The circuit below shows a device that has an alarm light under certain temperature conditions.

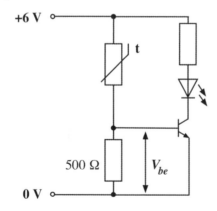

Calculate the voltage V_{be} across the base-emitter of the transistor:

a) in the cold when the resistance of the thermistor is 5.5 kΩ;

b) at 100°C when the resistance of the thermistor is 1 kΩ.

5.

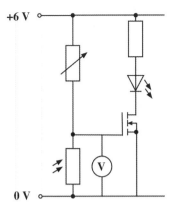

The variable resistor in the circuit above is set at 5 kΩ. In the light the LDR has a resistance of 1000 Ω but in the dark it increases to 25 kΩ.

Calculate the reading on the voltmeter:

a)   when the LDR is in light;

b)   when the LDR is in darkness.

6.

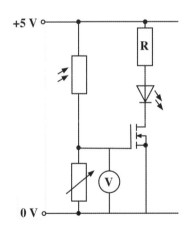

The LED is rated at 2 V, 15 mA.

Calculate the resistance of the resistor R required in the circuit.

PROPERTIES OF MATTER

Specific heat capacity (i)

For some of the questions in this section, you will have to use the information from the table 'Specific heat capacity of materials' shown in the Data Sheet on pages i and ii.

1. a) State the equation that links **heat** with **specific heat capacity**, **mass** and **temperature change** of a substance.

    b) State the symbol for each quantity.

    c) State the unit for each quantity, and its abbreviation.

In each of the following questions, assume that no energy is lost to the surroundings.

2. 4.8 kJ of energy raises the temperature of 1 kg of a liquid by 2 °C.

    a) What is the energy required to raise the temperature of 4 kg of the liquid by 2 °C?

    b) What is the energy required to raise the temperature of 4 kg of the liquid by 6 °C?

3. Calculate the energy required to heat 2.5 kg of water from room temperature (20 °C) to its boiling point.

4. A 1.2 kg block of metal is heated from 20 °C to 80 °C when 64 800 J of energy are supplied.

    a) Calculate the specific heat capacity of this metal.

    b) Identify the metal.

5. When 70 kJ of energy is supplied to a block of lead at 30 °C, its temperature is raised to 190 °C

    Calculate the mass of the block.

6. A block of aluminium with a mass of 2.5 kg is supplied with 7.5 x 10⁵ J of energy. The initial temperature is 20 °C.

    Calculate the final temperature of the aluminium.

7. Calculate the rise in temperature produced by supplying 1.5×10^5 J of energy:

   a) to 2.5 kg of lead;

   b) to 500 g of water.

8. Calculate the energy required:

   a) to raise the temperature of 3.6 kg of aluminium by 75 °C;

   b) to raise the temperature of 100 g of iron by 40 °C.

9. In an experiment to measure the specific heat capacity of a metal, the results were:

Energy supplied	=	7800 J
Mass of metal	=	650 g
Initial temperature	=	16 °C
Final temperature	=	47 °C

   a) Use these results to calculate the specific heat capacity for the metal.

   b) Identify the metal.

10. 500 g of water at 80 °C is mixed with 500 g of water at 20 °C.

    What is the final temperature of the mixture.

11. 500 g of water at 80 °C is mixed with 250 g of water at 20 °C.

    What is the final temperature of the mixture?

12. A 400 g copper block is heated in a Bunsen flame and then dropped into 750 g of water. The water is initially at 20 °C and after the copper is added the water reaches a final temperature of 52 °C.

    Calculate the temperature change of the copper.

Specific heat capacity (ii)

In each of the following questions, assume that no energy is lost to the surroundings.

1. A can contains 3.0 kg of water that is heated by a 2.0 kW heater for 360 s.

   Calculate the change in temperature that would occur.

2. A copper block of mass 4.0 kg is heated from 16 °C to its melting point at 1085 °C using a 7.5 kW heater.

   a) Calculate the energy that is needed to heat the copper block to its melting point.

   b) i) Calculate the time taken to heat the copper block.

   ii) In practice would this take a longer, shorter, or the same time, as calculated in part b) i)?

3. The current in a mains heater (230 V) is 10.2 A. The heater is switched on for 8 minutes. It is used to heat water from 20 °C to boiling point.

   Calculate the mass of water.

4. An aluminium container of mass 2.5 kg contains 1.7 kg of water at room temperature (18 °C). Both the container and the water are heated using a 1.5 kW heater to a temperature of 60 °C.

   a) i) Calculate the energy that is required to heat the water.

   ii) Calculate the energy that is required to heat the container.

   iii) What is the total energy that is required?

   b) Calculate the time taken.

5. A copper container of mass 1.2 kg contains 700 g of water.
   Both the container and the water are heated from 20 °C to 100 °C.
   The heater used is rated at 36 V, 8.0 A.

   a) Calculate the total energy that is required.

   b) Calculate the time taken.

6. A block of copper of mass 2.0 kg is heated by a mains heater.
    The current in the heater is 13 A for 3 minutes 30 seconds.
    The block is initially at 20 °C.

    a) Calculate the energy given to the copper block.

    b) Calculate the final temperature of the copper block.

7. The graph shows the way that the temperature of 2.05 kg of a liquid varies
    with time when heated with a 500 W heater.

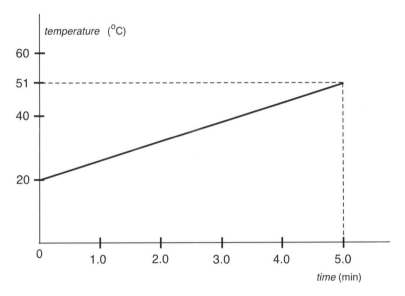

    a) Use this data to calculate the specific heat capacity of the liquid.

    b) Identify the liquid.

Latent heat (i)

For some of the questions in this section, you will have to use the information in the tables *'Specific latent heat of fusion / vaporisation'* shown in the Data Sheet on pages i and ii.

1. a) State the equation that links **heat** with **specific heat of fusion / vaporisation** and **mass** of a material.

    b) State the symbol for each quantity.

    c) State the unit for each quantity, and its abbreviation.

2. Each of the following is at its melting point.

    Calculate the energy required:

    a) to melt 5.0 kg of ice;

    b) to melt 0.10 kg of carbon dioxide;

    c) to melt 200 g of aluminium.

3. Each of the following is at its boiling point.

    Calculate the energy required:

    a) to vaporise 100 kg of glycerol;

    b) to vaporise 0.5 kg of water;

    c) to vaporise 20 g of turpentine.

4. Calculate the energy given out:

    a) when 0.1 kg of water freezes at its melting point;

    b) when 200 g of steam condenses at its boiling point.

5. It takes 27 kJ to melt 500 g of a certain solid at its melting point.
    Calculate the specific latent heat of fusion of the solid.

6. It takes 16.8 kJ to vaporise 20 g of a certain liquid at its boiling point.
    Calculate the specific latent heat of vaporisation of the liquid.

7. Calculate the mass of copper at its melting point that is melted by 82 000 J of energy.

8. Calculate the mass of alcohol at its boiling point that is vaporised by 56 000 J of energy.

Latent heat (ii)

For some of the questions in this section, you will have to use the information in the tables 'Specific latent heat of fusion / vaporisation' shown in the Data Sheet on pages i and ii.

In questions 1 to 8 in this section, assume that all the energy from the heater is absorbed by the material in the question.

1. A block of iron is heated to its melting point by a 1.5 kW heater.
   It takes a further 2 minutes for the iron to completely melt.

   Calculate the mass of the iron block.

2. A sample of glycerol is heated to its boiling point by a 4.5 kW heater.
   It takes a further 130 s for the glycerol to completely vaporise.

   Calculate the mass of the glycerol in the sample.

3. A block of ice of mass 3.0 kg is at 0 °C.
   It is heated until it becomes steam at 100 °C.

   a) i) Calculate the energy that is needed to melt the ice.

   ii) Calculate the energy that is needed to heat the water to its boiling point.

   iii) Calculate the energy that is needed to vaporise the water.

   b) What is the total energy required?

4. A 2 kg sample of alcohol at its melting point of -98 °C is heated until it becomes a gas at its boiling point of 65 °C.

   a) i) Calculate the energy that is needed to melt the alcohol .

   ii) Calculate the energy that is needed to heat the alcohol to its boiling point.

   iii) Calculate the energy that is needed to vaporise the alcohol.

   b) What is the total energy required?

5. A 300 g sample of liquid glycerol at 30 °C is heated until it becomes a gas at its boiling point of 290 °C.

   Take the specific heat capacity of glycerol to be 2430 J kg⁻¹ °C⁻¹.

   Calculate the total energy required.

6. A 70 g block of ice at -50 °C is heated until it becomes steam at 100 °C.

   Calculate the total energy required.

7. The graph shows how the temperature of 800 g of solid wax varies with time when heated with a 300 W heater.

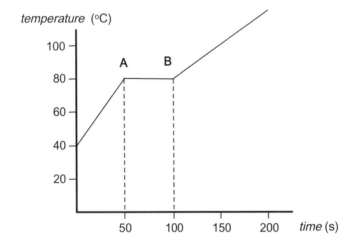

a) Explain what is happening to the wax in the region **AB**.

b) Calculate the specific latent heat of fusion of the wax.

8. The graph shows how the temperature of 75 g of a material varies with time when heated with a 36 W heater.

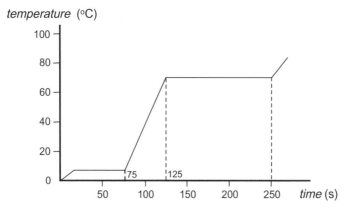

temperature (°C)

a) i) What is the approximate melting point of the solid?
   ii) What is the approximate boiling point of the liquid?
b) Calculate the specific latent heat of vaporisation for the material.
c) Calculate the approximate specific heat capacity for the liquid.

9. A scald from steam can be more damaging to the skin than a scald from boiling water.

   a) Calculate the energy given out when 0.10 g of liquid water at 100 °C cools to skin temperature at 30 °C.

   b) Calculate the extra energy given out when 0.10 g of steam changes to liquid water at 30 °C.

   c) Using your answers to a) and b), explain why a scald from steam can be more damaging than one from boiling water.

10. When a lead ball of mass 50 g is dropped on to a hard surface the ball comes to a stop and the ball heats up.

   Assuming all the kinetic energy is transferred to internal energy in the ball, from what height must the ball be dropped to raise its temperature by 0.20 °C?

11. An ice cream maker can remove heat at 145 J s⁻¹. A sample of liquid ice cream of mass 0.80 kg, at a temperature of 24 °C, is added to the container.

   a) i)   Calculate the energy that has to be removed from the sample to cool it to its freezing point of -16 °C.

   (Take the specific heat capacity of the ice cream to be 3220 J kg⁻¹ °C⁻¹.)

   ii) Calculate the energy that has to be removed from the sample to freeze the ice cream.

   (Take the specific latent heat of fusion of the ice cream to be 2.34×10^5 J kg⁻¹.)

   b) What is the total time taken to cool and freeze the ice cream?

   c) What assumption is made in the calculation for part b)?

12. a) While camping in winter, an explorer needs to melt frozen snow to provide boiling water. Frozen snow of mass 500 g and a temperature of 0 °C is placed in a 390 g aluminium container.
        In raising the temperature of the water to 100 °C, the average temperature of the container increases by 70 °C.

        Calculate the minimum energy that is needed to provide boiling water from the frozen snow.

   b) The energy is provided at 800 J s⁻¹.

        What is the minimum time that will be required to provide the boiling water from the snow?

Pressure

1. a) State the equation that links **pressure** with **force** and **surface area**.
   b) State the symbol for each quantity.
   c) State the unit for each quantity, and its abbreviation.

2. Calculate the pressure produced by each of the following.
   a) A 25 N force acting on an area of 10 m².
   b) A 3.0 kN force acting on an area of 4.0 m².
   c) A 2.8 N force acting on an area of 2.0 cm².

3. Calculate the force that produces each of the following.
   a) A pressure of 2.4×10^3 Pa on an area of 4.0 m².
   b) A pressure of 8.0×10^6 Pa on an area of 15 m².
   c) A pressure of 6.5×10^6 Pa on an area of 10 mm².

4. Calculate the area on which each of the following forces is acting to result in the given pressure.
   a) A force of 84 N producing a pressure of 70 Pa.
   b) A force of 2.0 kN producing a pressure of 100 Pa.
   c) A force of 4.2×10^4 N producing a pressure of 5.0 kPa.

5. The pressure outside an aircraft in flight is 7.0×10^4 Pa, while the pressure inside is 1.0×10^5 Pa.

   Calculate the force on a window of surface area 0.18 m².

6. Calculate the force on a table 2.4 m by 0.8 m, caused by an atmospheric pressure of 100 kPa.

7. A student weighs 540 N and is wearing stiletto heels. Each heel has an area of 5.0×10^{-5} m².

   Calculate the pressure exerted when balancing on the **two** heels.

8. A person with a mass of 50 kg exerts a force that is half their weight to push a drawing pin into a cork board. The pressure on the point of the drawing pin is 2.5×10^9 Pa.

   Calculate the surface area of the point of the drawing pin.

The gas laws: pressure and volume

1. A fixed mass of gas at pressure P_1 with a volume of V_1 has its pressure and volume changed to P_2 and V_2 respectively, without a change in temperature. State the relationship between P_1, V_1, P_2 and V_2.

2. a) Sketch a graph of volume against pressure for a fixed mass of gas at a constant temperature.

    b) Sketch a graph of 1/volume against pressure for a fixed mass of gas at a constant temperature.

3. A sample of gas of volume 100 mm³ is in a syringe. The gas is at a pressure of 1.6×10^5 Pa and is kept at a constant temperature.

    Calculate the pressure:

    a) when the volume of the gas is decreased to 25 mm³;

    b) when the volume of the gas is increased to 200 mm³.

4. a) A balloon containing 3.0 m³ of helium at 1.0 atmosphere is released and rises until the pressure of the helium is reduced to 0.20 atmospheres.

    Calculate the new volume.

    b) What assumption is being made in the calculation for part a)?

5. A sample of gas in an expandable container has a volume of 0.4 m³. The gas is at a pressure of 1.6 atmospheres and the temperature is kept constant.

    a) Calculate the new volume:

    i)   when the pressure is increased by 0.40 atmospheres;

    ii) when the pressure is decreased by 0.40 atmospheres.

    b) Calculate the new pressure:

    i)   when the volume is increased by 0.60 m³;

    ii) when the volume is decreased by 0.20 m³.

6. A sample of gas is contained in a cylinder fitted with a pressure gauge and a piston. The gas is kept at a constant temperature.

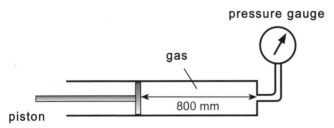

The initial pressure of the gas is 4.0 x 10⁵ Pa.

a) The piston is moved in until the pressure is 6.4 x 10⁵ Pa.

Calculate the new length of the column of gas.

b) The piston is moved back out to give the original pressure and volume.

Calculate the new pressure of the gas:

i) when the piston is moved out by 200 mm;

ii) when the piston is moved in by 600 mm.

The gas laws: volume and temperature

1. A fixed mass of gas with volume V_1 at a temperature T_1 has its volume and temperature changed to V_2 and T_2 respectively, without a change in pressure.

    a) State the relationship between V_1, T_1, V_2 and T_2.

    b) What scale of temperature must be used with this relationship?

2. a) Sketch a graph of volume (y-axis) against temperature in degrees Celsius (x-axis) for a fixed mass of gas.
    Use a temperature scale of 0 °C to 100 °C and project back to meet the y-axis.

    b) Sketch a graph of volume (y-axis) against temperature in kelvin (x-axis) for a fixed mass of gas.
    Use a temperature scale of 0 K to 400 K.

3. Convert each of the following temperatures on the Celsius scale to a reading on the Kelvin scale.

    a) 0 °C

    b) 27 °C

    c) 100 °C

    d) -73 °C

    e) 73 °C

    f) -150 °C

4. Convert each of the following temperatures on the Kelvin scale to a reading on the Celsius scale.

    a) 300 K

    b) 73 K

    c) 0 K

    d) 600 K

    e) 153 K

    f) 900 K

5. The temperature of an object rises by 27 °C.

    What is this temperature rise on the Kelvin scale?

6. The volume of a fixed mass of gas at a constant pressure is 100 litres when the temperature is 300 K.

   Calculate the new volume at each of the following temperatures.

   a) 600 K

   b) 150 K

   c) 450 K

   d) 273 K

7. The volume of a fixed mass of gas at a constant pressure is 250 litres when the temperature is 300 K.

   Calculate the new temperature, on the Kelvin scale, for each of the following volumes.

   a) 125 litres

   b) 500 litres

   c) 325 litres

   d) 210 litres

8. A fixed mass of gas has a volume of 4.0 m^3 at a temperature of 27 °C. The pressure is kept constant.

   Calculate the new volume at each of the following temperatures.

   a) 54 °C

   b) 327 °C

   c) 150 °C

   d) -80 °C

9. A fixed mass of gas occupies a volume of 0.30 m^3 at 0 °C.

   Calculate the temperature, on the Kelvin scale, when the volume is 0.50 m^3, assuming the pressure is constant.

10. A sample of a gas of fixed mass 17 g occupies a volume of 0.24 m^3 at 27 °C.

    a) Calculate the volume of the sample at 177 °C.

    b) What assumption is being made in the calculation for part a)?

The gas laws: pressure and temperature

1. A fixed mass of gas at pressure P_1 and a temperature T_1 has its pressure and temperature changed to P_2 and T_2 respectively, without a change in volume.

    a) State the relationship between P_1, T_1, P_2 and T_2.

    b) What scale of temperature must be used with this relationship?

2. a) Sketch a graph of pressure (y-axis) against temperature in degrees Celsius (x-axis) for a fixed mass of gas.
        Use a temperature scale of 0 °C to 100 °C and project back to meet the y-axis.

    b) Sketch a graph of pressure (y-axis) against temperature in kelvin (x-axis) for a fixed mass of gas.
        Use a temperature scale of 0 K to 400 K.

3. A fixed volume and mass of gas has a pressure of 48 kPa when the temperature is 400 K.

    Calculate the new pressure at each of the following temperatures.

    a) 800 K

    b) 100 K

    c) 273 K

    d) 437 K.

4. A fixed volume and mass of gas has a pressure of 120 kPa when the temperature is 300 K.

    Calculate the new temperature, on the Kelvin scale, at each of the following pressures.

    a) 100 kPa

    b) 54 kPa

    c) 72 kPa

    d) 150 kPa

5. A fixed volume and mass of air has a pressure of 100 kPa when the temperature is 27 °C.

Calculate the new pressure at each of the following temperatures.

a) 280 °C

b) 150 °C

c) 54 °C

d) 327 °C

6. A fixed volume and mass of air has a pressure of 1.5×10^5 Pa when the temperature is 57 °C.

Calculate the new temperature, in degrees Celsius, at each of the following pressures.

a) 2.0×10^5 Pa

b) 1.0×10^5 Pa

c) 3.0×10^5 Pa

d) 2.8×10^5 Pa

7. A test tube contains air at 1.0×10^5 Pa and 27 °C. The test tube has a cork at the mouth. When the test tube is heated in a water bath, the cork pops out when the temperature of the air in the test tube has reached 87 °C.

Calculate the pressure of the gas in the test tube when this occurs.

8. A fixed mass of gas has a pressure of 85 kN m^{-2} at a temperature of 20 °C. The volume is fixed.

a) i)   Calculate the temperature, in degrees Celsius, when the pressure is 100 kN m^{-2}.

    ii) Calculate the pressure when the temperature is -60 °C.

b) What assumption is being made in the calculations for part a)?

General gas equation

1. A fixed mass of gas is at pressure P_1, temperature T_1 and volume V_1.
   These values are changed to P_2, T_2 and V_2 respectively.
   State the relationship between P_1, T_1, V_1, P_2, T_2 and V_2.

2. A gas cylinder contains 20 litres of gas at a pressure of 8.0×10^5 Pa and a temperature of 127 °C.
   Calculate the new volume of the gas at a pressure of 1.0×10^5 Pa and a temperature of 27 °C.

3. A fixed mass of gas of volume 30 m³ at a temperature of 27 °C and a pressure of 98 kPa is heated to a temperature of 54 °C.
   The volume increases to 45 m³.
   Calculate the new pressure of the gas.

4. A fixed mass of gas of volume 50 m³ at a pressure of 150 kPa and a temperature of 27 °C is heated. The volume increases to 150 m³ and the pressure to 350 kPa.
   Calculate the new temperature of the gas, on the Kelvin scale.

5. The volume of a fixed mass of gas at a temperature of 127 °C is 800 m³.
   The pressure of the gas is halved and its temperature decreases to 27 °C.
   Calculate the new volume of the gas at a temperature of 27 °C.

6. The pressure of a fixed mass of a gas at a temperature of 50 °C is doubled and the volume halved.
   Calculate the new temperature of the gas, in degrees Celsius.

7. A sample of gas has a volume of 120 m³. The pressure on the sample is doubled and its temperature on the Kelvin scale also doubled.
   Calculate the new volume of the gas.

8. The volume of air in a pump is compressed from 0.60 m³ to 0.080 m³ and its pressure rises from 1.0×10^5 Pa to 1.2×10^6 Pa. The original temperature of the air is 27 °C.
   Calculate the new temperature of the air in the pump, in degrees Celsius.

9. A fixed mass of gas is at atmospheric pressure. Its volume is halved and its temperature on the Kelvin scale is tripled.
   Calculate the effect of these changes on the pressure of the gas.

Mixed gas laws problems

1. A balloon contains 4.0 m^3 of air at 27 $^{\circ}$C. When it is placed in a refrigerated room, it shrinks to a volume of 3.6 m^3.

    Calculate the temperature of the room, in degrees Celsius, assuming the pressure is constant.

2. A sample of a gas with a volume of 25 litres has a pressure of 4.0 x 10^7 Pa.

    Calculate the volume of the gas at a pressure of 5.0 x 10^5 Pa, assuming the temperature is constant.

3. A gas bubble has a volume of 15 mm^3 at a pressure of 100 kPa and a temperature of 7.0 $^{\circ}$C. When the pressure is reduced to 80 kPa, the volume increases to 25 mm^3.

    Calculate the new temperature of the gas, in degrees Celsius.

4. The gas in a used aerosol can is at a pressure of 1.0 x 10^5 Pa at 27 $^{\circ}$C. The can will explode when the temperature reaches 420 $^{\circ}$C.

    Calculate the pressure at which the can will explode.

5. A sealed syringe contains 50 mm^3 of gas at a temperature of 20 $^{\circ}$C and a pressure of 100 kPa. When the piston is depressed, the volume of gas decreases to 30 mm^3 and the temperature rises by 3.0 $^{\circ}$C.

    Calculate the new pressure of the gas.

6. A tank contains air at a pressure of 5.0 atmospheres at room temperature (20 $^{\circ}$C). It is fitted with a safety valve that releases air when the pressure reaches 9.0 atmospheres.

    Calculate the temperature of the air, on the Celsius scale, when the valve activates.

7. A sample of gas has a volume of 0.16 m^3 and a temperature of 27 $^{\circ}$C. The gas is heated to 177 $^{\circ}$C and the pressure is doubled.

    Calculate the new volume of the gas.

8. A fixed mass of gas is at a temperature of 20 $^{\circ}$C. When the temperature is changed, the volume of the gas increases four times and its pressure is halved.

    Calculate the new temperature of the gas, in degrees Celsius.

WAVES

Some wave parameters

1. a)   State what is meant by the **amplitude** of a wave.

    b)   State the symbol for amplitude.

2. a)   State what is meant by the **wavelength** of a wave.

    b)   State the symbol for wavelength.

3. a)   State what is meant by the **frequency** of a wave.

    b)   State the symbol for frequency.

    c)   State the unit for frequency, and its abbreviation.

4. a)   State the relationship between **wave period** and **frequency**.

    b)   State the symbol for wave period.

    c)   State the unit for wave period, and its abbreviation.

5. For each of the following:

    a)   state the amplitude of the waves;

    b)   state the wavelength of the waves.

    i)

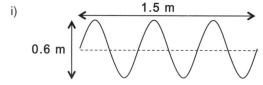

    ii)

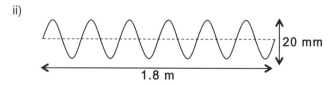

6. In a swimming pool 26 waves pass a point in 4.0 s.

    a)   Calculate the frequency of the waves.

    b)   Calculate the period of the waves.

7. In a water tank 1200 waves pass a point in 1 minute.

 a) Calculate the frequency of the waves.

 b) Calculate the period of the waves.

8.

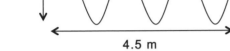

4 m

4.5 m

 a) i) What is the amplitude of the waves?

 ii) What is the wavelength of the waves?

 b) The waves shown take 2.0 s to pass a point.

 i) Calculate the frequency of the waves.

 ii) Calculate the period of the waves.

9. A tuning fork produces 840 vibrations in 2 minutes.
 Calculate the frequency of the note produced.

10.

48 mm

10 mm

 a) i) What is the amplitude of the waves?

 ii) What is the wavelength of the waves?

 b) The waves shown take 2×10^{-3} s to pass a point.

 i) Calculate the frequency of the waves.

 ii) Calculate the period of the waves.

11. A boat is anchored at sea and 12 complete waves pass the boat in 1 minute.
 The crests are 18 m apart on average.

 a) What is the wavelength of the waves?

 b) i) Calculate the frequency of the waves.

 ii) Calculate the period of the waves.

12. The distance from **A** to **B** is 2.16 m.
    The distance from **X** to **Y** is 0.04 m.

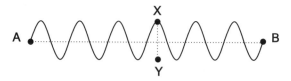

a) i)   What is the amplitude of the waves?

    ii) What is the wavelength of the waves?

b) The waves shown pass a point in 5 μs.

    i)   Calculate the frequency of the waves.

    ii) Calculate the period of the waves.

13. A child produces waves by throwing a stone into a pool of still water.
    After 4.0 s, the position of the crests are as shown.

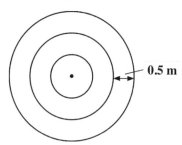

0.5 m

a) What is the wavelength of the waves?

b) Calculate the frequency of the waves.

Wave speed (i)

For some of the questions in this section, you will have to use the speed of sound in air and/or the speed of light in air. These are shown in the Data Sheet on pages i and ii.

1. a) State the equation that links **wave speed** with **distance** and **time**.
   b) State the symbol for each quantity.
   c) State the unit for each quantity, and its abbreviation.

2. Calculate the time taken for sound to travel 5.1 km.

3. A farmer in a field hears the sound of gunfire 3.6 s after a gun is fired.
   Calculate the distance of the farmer from the position of the gunfire.

4. The sound of an explosion in a quarry is heard 8.05 s later in a house that is 2.72 km away from the quarry.
   Use this information to calculate the speed of sound.

5. Sprinter **A** is 3.0 m away from the starting gun; sprinter **B** is 12 m away.
   Calculate the time advantage that sprinter **A** has on sprinter **B** on hearing the sound of the gun.

6. An observer of a storm hears the sound of thunder 10 s after lightning is seen.
   Calculate the distance from the observer to the storm, in kilometres.

7. A supersonic aircraft flies at 1.75 times the speed of sound.
   a) What is the speed of the aircraft in kilometres / hour?
   b) Calculate the time taken by the aircraft to fly 120 km.

8. Calculate the distance travelled, in metres:
   a) by sound in 15 s;
   b) by light in 1 minute.

9. Calculate the time taken for light to travel from the Sun to Earth, a distance of 1.5×10^8 km.

10. It takes a light signal 0.25 μs to travel between two mirrors.

    Calculate the distance between the mirrors.

11. The sound from a volcanic eruption is heard 70 s later by an observer who is 24 km away from the volcano.

    a) Use this information to calculate the speed of sound.

    b) Calculate the time taken for the light from the eruption to travel to the observer .

12. Carol and Peter both listen to a singer at a big event.
    Carol has a ticket and she is 180 m away from the loudspeaker.
    Peter is 7250 km away in another country.
    Carol hears the sound directly and Peter has to listen on his radio.

    a) Calculate the time taken for the sound to be heard by Carol.

    b) Calculate the time taken for the sound to be heard by Peter.

13. A girl is standing in front of a vertical cliff wall.
    She shouts and hears the echo 0.80 s later.

    a) Calculate the total distance travelled by the sound.

    b) How far is she standing from the cliff?

14. A sonar pulse travels through water at 1500 m s^{-1} and reflects from a shoal of fish. Two pulses are received at 1.0 s and 2.4 s after sending.

    a) Calculate the depth of the water.

    b) Calculate the depth at which the fish are swimming.

15. A doctor sends a pregnant woman for an ultrasound scan.
    One pulse is sent into her body and returns to the detector after 3.0 x 10^{-5} s. The speed of ultrasound in the body is 1575 m s^{-1}.

    Calculate the total distance that the pulse travels in her body.

Wave speed (ii)

1. a) State the equation that links **wave speed** with **frequency** and **wavelength**.

   b) State the symbol for each quantity.

   c) State the unit for each quantity, and its abbreviation.

2. Calculate the wave speed for each of the following waves.

   a) A wave with a frequency of 48 Hz and a wavelength of 1.6 m.

   b) A wave with a frequency of 1500 Hz and a wavelength of 4.5 m.

   c) A wave with a frequency of 1.7 kHz and a wavelength of 0.7 m.

3. Calculate the wavelength for each of the following waves.

   a) A wave with a speed of 100 m s^{-1} and a frequency of 10 Hz.

   b) A wave with a speed of 175 m s^{-1} and a frequency of 25 kHz.

   c) A wave with a speed of 18 m s^{-1} and a frequency of 900 Hz.

4. Calculate the frequency for each of the following waves.

   a) A wave with a speed of 38 m s^{-1} and a wavelength of 6.0 m.

   b) A wave with a speed of 72 m s^{-1} and a wavelength of 0.60 m.

   c) A wave with a speed of 9.0 m s^{-1} and a wavelength of 120 mm.

5. A long wave radio signal has a wavelength of 200 m and travels at the speed of light.

   Calculate the frequency of the signal.

6. A wave has a wavelength of 1.5×10^{-3} m and a frequency of 20 kHz.

   Calculate the wave speed.

7. A type of light in the visible spectrum has a frequency of 4.5×10^{14} Hz.

   Calculate the wavelength of this light.

8. In 5 minutes, 1800 waves pass a point. Each has a wavelength of 7.5 mm.

   Calculate the wave speed.

9. Travelling at 130 m s^{-1}, 780 waves pass a point in 30 s.

   Calculate the wavelength of the waves.

Mixed wave problems

1. The number of waves that pass a point in 6.0 s is calculated to be 420. The wavelength of the waves is 30 mm.

    a) Calculate the frequency of the waves.

    b) Calculate the wave speed.

2. Waves produced by a wave machine travel 30 m in 4.0 s. The wavelength of the waves of 250 mm.

    a) Calculate the speed of the waves.

    b) i) Calculate the frequency of the waves

        ii) Calculate the period of the waves.

3. An observer notes that 36 waves hit a beach every minute. The distance between the crests is 1.2 m.

    a) What is the wavelength of the waves?

    b) Calculate the frequency of the waves.

    c) Calculate the wave speed.

4. Certain waves that travel 72 km in 30 minutes have a wavelength of 0.08 m.

    a) Calculate the wave speed.

    b) i) Calculate the frequency of the waves.

        ii) Calculate the period of the waves.

5. A wave machine in a swimming pool delivers waves every 20 s. The wavelength of the waves is 7.0 m.

    a) Calculate the frequency of the waves.

    b) Calculate the wave speed.

6. Certain waves have a frequency of 900 kHz and a wavelength of 3.0 mm.

    a) Calculate the period of the waves.

    b) i) Calculate the wave speed.

        ii) Calculate the distance that the waves travel in 20 s.

7. Certain waves have a frequency of 270 Hz and a wavelength of 90 μm.

   a) Calculate the period of the wave.

   b) i) Calculate the wave speed.

      ii) Calculate the distance that the waves travel in 5 minutes.

8. Certain waves have a period of 5.0×10^{-4} s and a wavelength of 75 mm.

   a) Calculate the frequency of the waves.

   b) i) Calculate the wave speed.

      ii) Calculate the time that the waves take to travel 30 m.

9. The number of waves that pass a point in 4.0 s is calculated to be 28.
   The waves travel 90 m in 6 minutes.

   a) Calculate the wave speed.

   b) Calculate the frequency of the waves.

   c) Calculate the wavelength of the waves.

10. Certain waves have a wavelength of 7.0 mm and a frequency of 80 kHz.

    Calculate the time that the waves take to travel 28 m.

11. Certain waves travel 150 m in 5 minutes and have a wavelength of
    2.0×10^{-6} m.

    Calculate the period of the waves.

12. The number of waves that pass a point in 30 s is calculated to be 150.
    The crests of the waves are 0.4 m apart.

    Calculate the distance that the wave travels in 12 minutes.

13. A type of light wave in the visible spectrum has a wavelength of 550 nm.

    Calculate the distance that this light travels in 4.0×10^{-3} s.

14. A pulse of light, with a wavelength of 6.4×10^{-7} m, travels through a thin glass
    cable at a speed of 2.0×10^{8} m s^{-1}.
    It takes the pulse 7.5×10^{-12} s to reach the end of the cable.

    a) i) Calculate the distance that the light travels in the cable.

       ii) Calculate the frequency of the light.

    b) Calculate the distance that the light would travel in air in the same time.

The electromagnetic spectrum

1. An electromagnetic radiation has a frequency of 94 MHz.

   a) Calculate the wavelength of the radiation .

   b) State which band of the electromagnetic spectrum includes this radiation .

2. An electromagnetic radiation has a frequency of 4.0×10^{16} Hz.

   a) Calculate the wavelength of the radiation .

   b) State which band of the electromagnetic spectrum includes this radiation .

3. An electromagnetic radiation has a wavelength of 5.0×10^{-8} m.

   a) Calculate the frequency of the radiation .

   b) State which band of the electromagnetic spectrum includes this radiation .

4. An electromagnetic radiation has a wavelength of 5.0×10^{-10} m.

   a) Calculate the frequency of the radiation .

   b) State which band of the electromagnetic spectrum includes this radiation .

5. Ultraviolet radiation travels from a star that is 5.0×10^{25} km away.

   Calculate the time it takes for the radiation to travel to the Earth.

RADIATION

Activity

1. a) State what is meant by one **becquerel**.

    b) State the symbol for the becquerel.

2. Calculate the activity of each of the following.

    a) A source in which 648 000 atoms decay in 3 minutes.

    b) A source in which 9.3×10^5 atoms decay in 5 minutes.

3. Calculate the number of decays that take place in each of the following.

    a) A source with an activity of 32 Bq in 5 minutes.

    b) A source with an activity of 7.5 MBq in 10 minutes.

4. Calculate the time taken for each of the following.

    a) An 18 kBq source to undergo 4.86×10^6 decays.

    b) A 6.3×10^3 Bq source to undergo 1.26×10^5 decays.

Absorbed dose

1. a) State the equation that links **absorbed dose**, **energy** and **mass**.

    b) State the symbol for each quantity.

    c) State the unit for each quantity, and its abbreviation.

2. Calculate the mass of each of the following.

    a) A sample of tissue that receives an absorbed dose of 180 mGy and 5.4×10^{-3} J of energy.

    b) A sample of tissue that receives an absorbed dose of 72 mGy and 3.24×10^{-2} J of energy.

3. Calculate the absorbed dose for each of the following.

    a) A sample of tissue of mass 0.066 kg that absorbs 1.2×10^{-2} J of energy.

    b) A sample of tissue of mass 120 g that absorbs 0.05 J of energy.

4. Calculate the energy that will be absorbed by each of the following.

    a) A sample of tissue of mass 0.042 kg with an absorbed dose of 70 mGy.

    b) A sample of tissue of mass 25 g with an absorbed dose of 40 mGy.

5. Worker **A** has a mass of 55 kg and absorbs 0.13 J of energy from a radioactive source; worker **B**, who has a mass of 72 kg and absorbs 0.15 J of energy from the same source.

    Show by calculation which worker has the greater absorbed dose.

Equivalent dose

For some of the questions in this section, you will use the information from the table *'Radiation weighting factors'* shown in the Data Sheet on pages i and ii.

1. a) State the equation that links **equivalent dose** with **absorbed dose** and **radiation weighting factor**.

   b) State the symbol for each quantity.

   c) State the unit for each quantity, and its abbreviation.

2. A sample of tissue is exposed to a total equivalent dose rate of 25 μSv min^{-1}. The exposure lasts for 18 minutes.

   What is the equivalent dose?

3. A worker is exposed to a total equivalent dose rate of 8.0 μSv h^{-1}. He works for 35 hours a week and for 48 weeks a year.

   a) What is the total equivalent dose for one week?

   b) What is the total equivalent dose for the year?

4. Calculate the equivalent dose for each of the following.

   a) A source of slow neutrons gives a sample an absorbed dose of 650 μGy.

   b) A source of fast neutrons gives a sample an absorbed dose of 12 mGy.

5. Calculate the absorbed dose for each of the following.

   a) An source of alpha radiation that produces an equivalent dose of 0.84 mSv.

   b) A source of beta radiation that produces an equivalent dose of 195 μSv.

6. Calculate the radiation weighting factor for the source in each of the following.

   a) An absorbed dose of 1.5 mGy of radiation, that gives an equivalent dose of 2.7 mSv.

   b) An absorbed dose of 360 μGy that gives an equivalent dose of 828 μSv.

7. Calculate the total equivalent dose for each of the following.

a) A worker who receives 20 μGy of alpha radiation and 250 μGy of gamma radiation.

b) A hospital technician who receives 20 μGy of fast neutrons and 40 μGy of slow neutrons.

c) A worker who receives 320 μGy of gamma radiation, 250 μGy of slow neutrons, 75 μGy of fast neutrons and 40 μGy of alpha radiation.

d) A patient who receives 15 μGy of alpha radiation and 20 μGy of fast neutrons.

8. A sample receives an absorbed dose of 0.54 mGy and an equivalent dose of 1.62 mSv from a single type of radiation.

a) Calculate the radiation weighting factor of the radiation.

b) Identify the type of this radiation.

9. During one year, a worker at a Nuclear Power Station is exposed to 2 mGy of fast neutrons, 500 μGy of alpha radiation, 3000 μGy of slow neutrons and 8 mGy of gamma radiation.
The equivalent dose limit for workers in the nuclear industry is 50 mSv per year.

Show by calculation whether this worker is within the safety limit for exposure to radiation.

10. A patient is exposed to 40 μGy of fast neutrons and 100 μGy of slow neutrons, both for 2.5 minutes.

a) Calculate the total equivalent dose of the radiation absorbed by the patient.

b) What is the equivalent dose rate in millisieverts per hour?

11. An sample of tissue receives an equivalent dose of 60 μSv from a gamma source. The mass of the tissue is 90 g.

Calculate the energy that is absorbed by the sample.

12. A tumour of mass 75 g absorbs 1.35×10^{-3} J of energy from a source of alpha radiation.

Calculate the equivalent dose of the absorbed radiation.

Half-life

1. Calculate the activity of each of the following after the stated time interval.

   a) A source with an original activity of 80 kBq, after 8.1 days; the half-life of the source is 2.7 days.

   b) A source with an original activity of 1200 MBq , after 7.2 hours; the half-life of the source is 1.8 hours.

   c) A source with an original activity of 9600 MBq , after 10 minutes; the half-life of the source is 2 minutes.

2. Calculate the original activity of each of the following sources.

   a) A source with an activity that has fallen to 17 kBq after 1140 days; the half-life of the source is 285 days.

   b) A source with an activity that has fallen to 28 MBq after 15.9 years; the half-life of the source is 5.3 years.

   c) A source with an activity that has fallen to 9 MBq after 75 hours; the half-life of the source is 15 hours.

3. Calculate the time for each the following decreases in activity.

   a) A source with an activity of 256 MBq to fall to an activity of 8 MBq; the half-life of the source is 60 days.

   b) A source with an activity of 512 mGy to fall to an activity of 1 mGy; the half-life of the source is 1 hour.

   c) A source with an activity of 80 MBq to fall to an activity of 2.5 MBq; the half-life of the source is 30 s.

4. Calculate the half-life of each the following sources.

   a) A source with an original activity of 10 MBq and an activity of 0.625 MBq after 24 hours.

   b) A source with an original activity of 4800 kBq and an activity of 150 kBq after 10 days.

   c) A source with an original activity of 24 kBq and an activity of 3 kBq after 6 s.

5. A source has a half-life of 3 hours.

Calculate the fraction of the original activity that remains:

a) after 6 hours;

b) after 15 hours.

6. A source has a half-life of 3.5 years.

Calculate the time taken:

a) for the activity to fall to one quarter of its original value;

b) for the activity to fall to one sixteenth of its original value.

7. A source produces an equivalent dose of 1.2 mSv after 12 days. The half-life of the source is 4 days.

Calculate the original equivalent dose.

8. A source has a half-life of 12 s and an activity of 9600 kBq.

Calculate the activity of the source 1 minute later.

9. Calculate the half-life of each of the following sources.

a) A source that gives an equivalent dose of 192 μSv. This falls to 3 μSv after 7.5 hours.

b) A source that gives an equivalent dose of 1024 μSv. This falls to 8 μSv after 1 hour 45 minutes.

10. Calculate the half-life of each of the following sources.

a) The activity of the source reduces to 6.25% of its original activity in 20 years.

b) The activity of the source reduces to 3.125% of its original activity in 45 hours.

11. Caesium-144 has a half-life of 285 days. After 1140 days, the activity of a sample has fallen to 17 kBq.

Calculate the original activity of the caesium.

12. Calculate the time for which each of the following sources can be of use.

    a) A gamma source with a half-life of 3 minutes is injected into a patient's body. The initial activity of the source is 640 Bq. A gamma camera cannot detect activity below 10 Bq.

    b) An iodine source has a half-life of 8 days.
       When delivered to the hospital it gives an absorbed dose of 1.2 mGy. The source is useful until the absorbed dose drops to 37.5 µGy.

13. The graph shows the activity of a sample of a radioisotope.

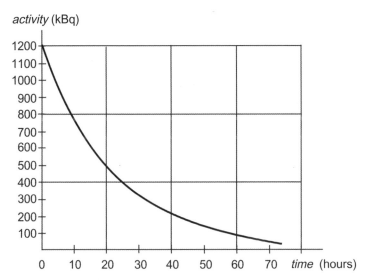

    a) i) What is the initial activity of this source?
       ii) How long does it take for the activity to fall to 300 kBq?
    b) Estimate the half-life of the radioisotope.

14. A technician records the corrected count rate from a radioactive sample of iodine at the same time each week.

Time elapsed (weeks)	0	1	2	3	4	5	6	7	8
Corrected count rate (counts/min)	500	320	196	128	84	48	28	20	12

    a) Plot a graph of the corrected count rate against time.
    b) Estimate the half-life of the source.

15. Calculate the half-life of each of the following sources.

    a) A source that contributes to a count rate that falls from 140 counts per minute to 35 counts per minute in 15 days; the background count rate is 20 counts per minute.

    b) A source that contributes to a count rate that falls from 920 counts per minute to 129 counts per minute in 24 hours; the background count rate is 16 counts per minute.

16. The decay graph for a radioactive substance is shown.

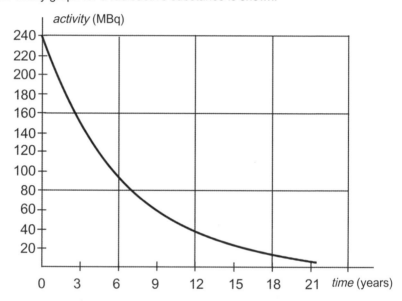

    Estimate the half-life of the source.

17. An experiment with a radioactive source was carried out in an area where there is a high background radiation. The results are shown:

Time (mins)	0	3	6	9	12	15	18	21	24	27	30	33
Count rate (cpm)	88	72	60	52	44	39	36	34	32	31	30	30

    a) i) What is the background count rate?

       ii) Plot a graph of the corrected count rate against time.

    b) Estimate the half-life of the source.

Significant figures

Give the answer to each of the following calculations to the **correct number of significant figures**.

1.   Calculate the speed of a trolley that travels a distance of 65 m in 2.2 s.

2.   Calculate the power of a toy machine that produces 8.7 J of energy in 4.0 s.

3.   A car starts from rest and reaches a speed of 35 m s^{-1} in 4.25 s.
     Calculate the acceleration of the car.

4.   Calculate the mass of rock that has a weight of 1430 N on Earth.

5.   Calculate the speed of a toy car, mass 75 kg, that is moving with a kinetic energy of 820 J.

6.   Calculate the resulting force that is acting on a vehicle, mass 1850 kg, that accelerates from rest at 0.17 m s^{-2}.

7.   A boy of mass 52.5 kg climbs up a hill and gains a height of 32.0 m.
     Calculate the gain in gravitational potential energy.

8.   Calculate the energy required to raise the temperature of 472 g of water by 10.4 °C.

9.   Calculate the energy required to melt a solid block of lead, mass 0.543 kg, that is at 328 °C (the melting point of lead).

10. A sample of gas, in an expandable container at a pressure of 1.4 atmospheres, has a volume of 0.40 m^3.
     Calculate the new volume when the pressure is increased to 1.7 atmospheres. (Assume that the temperature remains constant.)

11. A fixed volume of a gas has a pressure of 246 kPa at a temperature of 303 K.
     Calculate the new temperature, on the Kelvin scale, when the pressure is reduced to 70.4 kPa.

ANSWERS

DYNAMICS

Speed, distance and time (page 1)

1. a) 25 m s⁻¹
   b) 126 km h⁻¹
2. a) speed = distance / time
   b) $v = d/t$
   c) v is in metres per second, m s⁻¹
      d is in metres, m
      t is in seconds, s
3. a) 1.2 m s⁻¹
   b) 16 m s⁻¹
   c) 287 m s⁻¹
4. a) 160 s
   b) 1250 s
   c) 0.005 s
5. a) 3.6 m
   b) 56 m
   c) 4.5 m
6. a) 15 km h⁻¹
   b) 4.2 m s⁻¹
7. a) 0.112 m s⁻¹
   b) 2 m s⁻¹
8. a) 0.06 m s⁻¹
   b) 0.15 m

Vectors and scalar quantities (page 3)

1. a) 25 m west
   b) 115 m east
   c) 2 km south
2. a) i) 4.6 km
      ii) 3 km east
   b) i) 2.6 m s⁻¹
      ii) 1.7 m s⁻¹ east
3. a) i) 400 m
      ii) 0 m
   b) i) 6.2 m s⁻¹
      ii) 0 m s⁻¹
4. a) i) 122 km
      ii) 14 km south
   b) i) 61 km h⁻¹
      ii) 7 km h⁻¹ south
5. a) i) 210 km
      ii) 150 km at a bearing of 053
   b) i) 84 km h⁻¹
      ii) 60 km h⁻¹ at a bearing of 053
6. a) 500 m at a bearing of 037
   b) 13 m at a bearing of 023
   c) 985 m at a bearing of 204
7. a) 15 km at a bearing of 157
   b) 31 km at a bearing of 234
   c) 97 m at a bearing of 320
8. a) 2.5 m at a bearing of 127
   b) 3 m at a bearing of 221
   c) 11 m at a bearing of 190

Acceleration

1. a) acceleration =
      (final velocity – initial velocity)
                  / time

   b) $a = (v - u)/t$

   c) a is in metres per second per
      second, m s^{-2}
      v is in metres per second, m s^{-1}
      u is in metres per second, m s^{-1}
      t is in seconds, s

2. a) 2.5 m s^{-2}
   b) 4.5m s^{-2}
   c) 1.5 m s^{-2}
   d) 800 m s^{-2}
   e) 32 m s^{-2}
   f) -0.16 m s^{-2}
   g) -2.7×10^{-3} m s^{-2}
   h) 8.3 m s^{-2}
   i) 25 m s^{-2}
   j) 6.8 m s^{-2}
   k) -7.3 m s^{-2}
   l) -1120 m s^{-2}

3. a) -7.5 s
   b) 4.5 s
   c) 2.8 s

4. a) 25 m s^{-1}
   b) 8.8 m s^{-1}
   c) -3.8 m s^{-1}

5. a) 16 m s^{-1}
   b) 21 m s^{-1}
   c) -17 m s^{-1}

6. a) 0.75 m s^{-2}
   b) 12 s

7. a) 0.71 s
   b) 36 m s^{-1}

8. a) 17 m s^{-1}
   b) 7.9 s

9. a) 6.2 s
   b) -194 m s^{-2}

10. 4.1 s

Velocity (speed) - time graphs   (page 7)

1. a)   deceleration to rest
    b)   acceleration
    c)   constant speed

2.

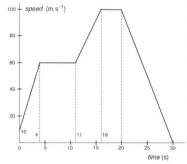

```
speed (m s⁻¹)
```

3. a)   accelerates from rest to
           15 ms⁻¹ in10 s;
           then constant speed for 40 s
    b)   1.5 m s⁻²
    c)   675 m

4. a)   21 m s⁻¹
    b)
    c)   472.5 m

5. a) i)   72 m
       ii) 247.5 m
       iii) 190 m
    b) i)   9 m s⁻¹
       ii) 12.4 m s⁻¹
       iii) 13.6 m s⁻¹

6. a)   **B** and **C**
    b) i)   0.9 m s⁻²
       ii) -1.9 m s⁻²
    c)   189 m
    d) i)   2214 m
       ii) 21 m s⁻¹

7. a) i)   deceleration from 12 m s⁻¹ to
            6 m s⁻¹ in 40 s
       ii) constant speed of 6 m s⁻¹
            for 20 s
       iii) deceleration from 6 m s⁻¹ to
            rest in 15 s

    b) i)   -0.15 m s⁻²
       ii) -0.4 m s⁻²
    c)   525 m

8. a)   constant speed of 4 m s⁻¹ for
           6 s; uniform acceleration from
           4 m s⁻¹ to 12 m s⁻¹ in 6 s;
           uniform deceleration from
           12 m s⁻¹ to rest in 6 s.
    b) i)   1.3 m s⁻²;
       ii) -2 m s⁻²
    c) i)   8 m s⁻¹
       ii) 6 m s⁻¹
    d)   108 m

9. a)
    b)   1860 m

10. a)   uniform acceleration from
           rest to 10 m s⁻¹ in 4 s; constant
           velocity for 5 s; uniform
           deceleration to rest in 4 s;
           uniform acceleration from
           rest to 12 m s⁻¹ in **reverse**
           direction in 5 s; constant
           velocity for 2 s; deceleration
           to rest in 2 s;
    b) i)   2.5 m s⁻²
       ii) -2.4 m s⁻²
       iii) 6 m s⁻²
    c) i)   156 m
       ii) 24 m original direction

11. a) 18 m s^{-1}; -10 m s^{-1}

b)

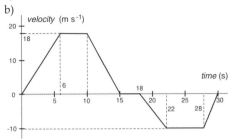

c) i) 261 m

   ii) 81 m original direction

12. a) constant velocity of 50 m s^{-1}
      for 10 s; uniform deceleration
      to rest in 2 s; hover position
      for 2 s, acceleration to 60 m s^{-1}
      in **reverse** direction in 3 s;
      constant velocity for 5 s;
      uniform deceleration to rest
      in 2 s.

b) i) -25 m s^{-2}

   ii) -20 m s^{-2}

   iii) 30 m s^{-2}

c) i) 1000 m

   ii) 100 m original direction

13. a) 9.6 m s^{-2}

b)

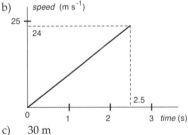

c) 30 m

14. a) i) -9.8 m s^{-2}

    ii) -9.8 m s^{-2}

b) 2 s

c) -19.6 m s^{-1}

d)

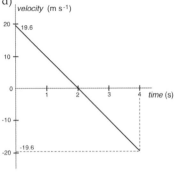

e) i) 39.2 m

   ii) 0 m

Weight   **(page 12)**

1. a) weight = mass x
        gravitational field strength

b) $W = mg$

c) W is in Newtons , N
    m is in kilograms, kg
    g is in newtons per kilogram,
                $N \text{ kg}^{-1}$

2. a) 24.5 N

b) 3680 N

3. a) 15 kg

b) 56 kg

4. a) **A** 9.8 N kg^{-1}
        B 1.6 N kg^{-1}

b) **A** Earth
        B Moon

5. a) 637 N

b) i) 65 kg

   ii) 1495 N

6. a) 20.3 kg

b) i) 20.3 kg

   ii) 75.1 N

7. 392 N

Resultant quantities   (page 13)

1. a) $2\,N \rightarrow$
   b) $12\,N \rightarrow$
   c) $2N \leftarrow$
   d) $8\,N \rightarrow$

2. a)   10 N at 37° to 6 N from 8 N
   b)   15 N at 37° to 5 N from 12 N
   c)   13 N at 67° to 12 N from 5 N
   d)   29 N at 49° to 25 N from 15 N

3. a) 8.5×10^5 N at a bearing of 021
   b)   170 N at a bearing of 090

4. a)   226 m s^{-1} at a bearing of 346
   b)   16.6 m s^{-1} at a bearing of 115

5. a)   294 N
   b)

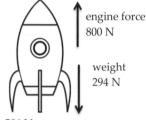

engine force
800 N

weight
294 N

   c)   506 N up

Newton's First Law   (page 15)

1. An object at rest stays at rest and an object in motion stays in motion with the same speed and in the same direction unless acted upon by an unbalanced force

2. a)   16 kN
   b)   6900 m

3.   274 N

4. a)   24.5 N
   b)   68 m

5.   17 km s^{-1}

6. a)   275 N
   b)   28 kg

7.   15 kg

Newton's Second Law   (page 16)

1. When the forces acting on a moving object are unbalanced, the object will accelerate.

2. a)   force = mass x acceleration
   b) $F = ma$
   c) F is in Newtons, N
        m is in grams, g
        m is in kilograms, kg
        a is in metres per second per second, m s^{-2}

3. a)   4.5 N
   b)   7.2 N
   c)   273 N

4. a)   180 m s^{-2}
   b)   84 m s^{-2}
   c)   4.1 m s^{-2}

5. a)   3.3 kg
   b)   4000 kg
   c)   13 000 kg

6.   20 m s^{-2}

7.   2860 N

8.   60 000 kg

9. a)   2.75 m s^{-2}
   b)   2475 N

10.   5 m s^{-2}

11.   680 kg

12.   120 N

13.   3.5 N

14. a) 4×10^6 N
    b)   13.6 m s^{-2}

Newton's Third Law   (page 18)

1. if **A** exerts a force on **B**, then **B** exerts an equal but opposite force on A, i.e. for every action there is an equal and opposite reaction.

2.   300 N

3. a)   150 N
   b)   150 N in the opposite direction

4. a)   135 N
   b)   135 N in the opposite direction
   c)   2.3 m s^{-2} in the opposite direction

Work done   (page 19)

1. a)   work done = force x distance
   b) $E_w = Fd$
   c) E_w is in joules, J
           F is in newtons, N
           d is in metres, m
2. a)   44 J
   b) 1.2×10^7 J   or 1.2×10^4 kJ
   c) 9×10^{-6} J
3. a)   30 N
   b)   4500 N
   c)   1400 N
4. a)   1250 m
   b)   920 m
   c)   120 000 m or 120 km
5. 9×10^6 J   or 9×10^3 kJ
6.   12 m
7.   240 N
8.   1.92 m
9. 1.5×10^9 J or 1.5×10^6 kJ
10.   8750 J
11.   24 000 J   or 24 kJ
12.   1200 m

Power, work done and time   (page 21)

1. a)   power = work done / time
   b) $P = E_w / t$
   c) P is in watts, W
           E_w is in joules, J
           t is in seconds, s
2. a)   1.8 W
   b)   4400 W or 4.4 kW
   c)   120 W
3. a)   9000 J or 9 kJ
   b)   3600 J or 3.6 kJ
   c) 5×10^5 J or 500 kJ
4. a)   25 s
   b)   2000 s
   c)   25 s
5.   35 W
6.   73 W
7.   30 s
8. 3.6×10^6 W or 3.6 MW

Gravitational potential energy   (page 22)

1. a)   gravitational potential energy
           = mass x gravitational field
              strength x height
   b) $E_p = mgh$
   c) E_p is in joules, J
           m is in kilograms, kg
           g is in newtons per kilogram, N kg^{-1}
           h is in metres, m
2. a)   883 J
   b)   0.11 J
   c) 4.9×10^8 J   or 4.9×10^5 kJ
3. a)   5.1 kg
   b)   0.24 kg
   c)   25 000 kg
4. a)   15 m
   b)   2.5 m
   c)   36 m
5.   1.5 kg
6.   62 m
7.   1.6 N kg^{-1}
8.   195 J
9.   9800 J

Kinetic energy   (page 24)

1. a)   kinetic energy = ½ mass x
                        (velocity)^2
   b) $E_k = \tfrac{1}{2}mv^2$
   c) E_k is in joules, J
           m is in kilograms, kg
           v is in metres per second, m s^{-1}
2. a)   18 J
   b)   2400 J
   c)   59 J
3. a)   3.8 kg
   b)   1500 kg
   c)   4.1 kg
4. a)   12 m s^{-1}
   b)   15 m s^{-1}
   c)   29 m s^{-1}
5.   1000 kg
6.   22 m s^{-1}

7. 0.27 J
8. a) i) 75 J
        ii) 300 J
    b) i) 1.97×10^6 J
        ii) 7.88×10^6 J
    c) The kinetic energy increases
        by a factor of 4.
9. 5100 J

Mixed dynamics problems (i)   (page 26)

1. a) i) 882 J
        ii) 147 J
    b) 1029 J
2. a) i) 17 640 J
        ii) 529 J
    b) 18 169 J
3. a) 281 J
    b) i) 281 J
        ii) 75 m s^{-1}
    c) i) All the potential energy is
        transformed into kinetic
        energy, i.e. no energy is lost.
4. a) 73.5 J
    b) i) 73.5 J
        ii) 7.7 m s^{-1}
5. a) 94 080 J
    b) 48 600 J
    c) 45 480 J
6. a) i) 5.88 J
        ii) 1.25 J
        iii) 7.13 J
    b) 6 m s^{-1}
7. a) 2.8 J
    b) 11 m
8. 14 m s^{-1}
9. 136 m s^{-1}
10. 49 m s^{-1}

Mixed dynamics problems (ii) (page 28)

1. a) 240 000 J
    b) 48 m
2. 2000 W
3. 1.26×10^6 J
4. a) Child **A** does more work than
        child **B** as child **A** has a
        greater weight.
    b) i) 320 W
        ii) 412 W
5. a) i) same
        ii) greater
    b) 1286 W
6. a) 390 000 J
    b) 13 kW
7. 11 kW
8. a) 192 kJ
    b) 10.7×10^3 W or 10.7 kW
9. a) 2916 J
    c) 833 W
10. a) i) 1750 kg
        ii) 336 m
    b) 5.8×10^6 J
    c) i) 48 kW
        ii) Energy is lost as heat due to
        friction.
11. 2439 W
12. 15 s
13. a) 3570 J
    b) 446 N
14. 31500 W
15. a) i) 388 kJ
        ii) 19 m s^{-1}
    b) i) 168 kJ
        ii) 6720 N
        iii) 14 m s^{-1}

16. a) 421 N
    b)

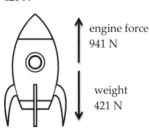

engine force
941 N

weight
421 N

    c) 12 m s⁻¹
17. a) 4.5 m s⁻²
    b) i) 18 m s⁻¹
       ii) 18 m s⁻¹
18. a) i) 1.4 m s⁻¹
       ii) 725 J
    b) 29 N
19. a)

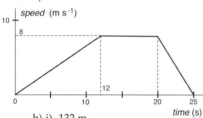

    b) i) 132 m
       ii) 2 N
       iii) 4.8 N
20.   5.4 x 10³ N
21.   15 m s⁻²
22. a) i) 0.5 m s⁻²
       ii) 4 m s⁻¹
    b) i) -2 m s⁻²
       ii) 5 N
       iii) 6.25 N
23.   7.84 N
24. a) 5780 N
    b) i) 280 kg
       ii) 84 kg
25. a) 4.9 x 10⁵ N
    b) 9.4 x 10⁵ N

26. a) i) 4.5 m s⁻²
       ii) 31.5 m s⁻¹
    b) 10.5 s
    c) i)

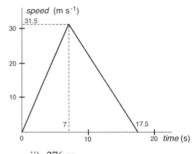

       ii) 276 m
27.

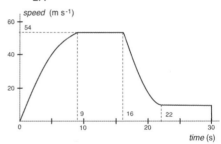

Projectile motion   **(page 33)**

1. a)   6.5 m s⁻¹
   b)   39.2 m s⁻¹
   c) i)

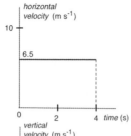

   ii)

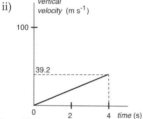

   d)   78.4 m

2. a)   1.6 m
   b)   4.9 m s⁻¹
   c) i)

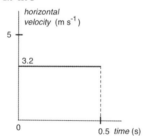

   ii)

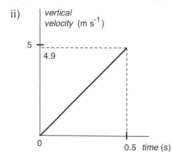

   d)   1.2 m

3. a)   108 m s⁻¹
   b) i)

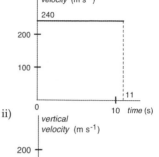

   ii)

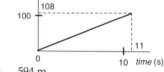

   c)   594 m
   d)   2640 m
4. a)   22.4 m
   b)   78.4 m s⁻¹
   c)   314 m
5. a)   88 m s⁻¹
   b)   396 m
6. a) i)   0 m s⁻¹
     ii)   9.8 m s⁻²
   b)   10 s
   c)   98 m s⁻¹
   d) i)

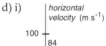
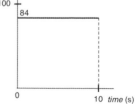

ii)

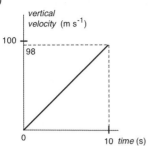

e) 490 m

7. a) 0.8 m s⁻¹

b) 15 m s⁻¹

c) i)

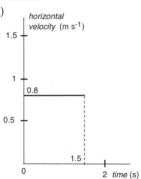

ii)

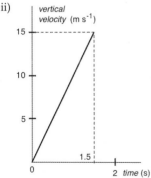

d) 11 m

8. a) 4.5 s

b) 44 m s⁻¹

c) 99 m

SPACE

Space travel and exploration   (page 36)

1.   434 N
2. 1.9×10^8 m
3. 1.5×10^{11} m
4. a) 5324 m s^{-1}
      b)   383 s
5.   0.24 s
6. a) 3.9×10^9 J
      b) 1.3×10^5 J
7. 2.7×10^9 J
8. a) 8.1×10^{10} J
      b) i)   200 m s^{-2}
        ii) 4.52×10^5 N   or 452 kN
      c) 4.74×10^5 N   or 474 kN
9. 1.4×10^{10} J
10.   81 W
11. 3×10^5 J kg^{-1}
12. a)   24 hours
      b)   2500 km
13. a) 6×10^9 J
      b)   3500 °C
14. a)   6000 N
      b) i)   14.4 m s^{-2}
        ii)   312.5 s
15. a) 2.2×10^6 J
      b) i) 6.3×10^4 J
        ii) 2.3×10^4 J

Light years   (page 39)

1. a) 9.5×10^{15} m
      b) 9.5×10^{20} m
2.   500 s
3. 5.8×10^{12} m
4. a) i)   4.3 light years
        ii) 4.1×10^{16} m
      b)   75 000 years
5. 4×10^{20} m

ELECTRICITY

Electrical current and voltage   (page 40)

1. a) I_1 0.9 A   b) V_1 5 V
        I_2 5 A V_2 15 V
        I_3 1.4 A V_3 5V
        I_4 1.4 A V_4 4 V
        I_5 2.5 A
        I_6 2 A
2. a) I_1 1.5 A   b) V_1 7 V
        I_2 2 A V_2 12 V
        I_3 2 A V_3 8V
        I_4 2 A V_4 8 V
        I_5 2 A
        I_6 0.8 A
3. a)   6 V
      b) i)   0.6 A
        ii)   0.2 A
        iii)   0.3 A

Series and parallel circuits   (page 42)

1. a) $R_T = R_1 + R_2 + R_3$
      b) $1/R_T = 1/R_1 + 1/R_2 + 1/R_3$
2. a)   24 Ω
      b)   2 k Ω
      c)   1750 Ω   or   1.75 k Ω
3. a)   3 Ω
      b)   5 Ω
      c)   1 Ω
      d)   30 Ω
4. a)   2 Ω
      b)   3 Ω
      c)   9 Ω
      d)   4 Ω
      e)   3.6 Ω
      f)   6.8 Ω
5. a)   10 Ω
      b)   5.4 Ω
      c)   10 Ω
      d)   9 Ω
6. a)   500 Ω
      b)   5 Ω

7. a) 36 Ω
   b) 16 Ω
8. a) 24 Ω
   b) 2.2 Ω
   c) 8.8 Ω
   d) 11 Ω
9. 20 Ω
10.

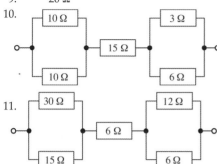

11.

12. a) E
    b) A

Ohms's Law (page 45)

1. a) 750 mV
   b) 3200 mV
   c) 0.87 V
   d) 2.963 V
   e) 0.00025 V or 2.5×10^{-4} V
   f) 40 000 μV or 4×10^4 μV
2. a) 120 000 mA or 1.2×10^5 mA
   b) 30 mA
   c) 5.805 A
   d) 0.002 A or 2×10^{-3} A
   e) 0.000756 A or 7.56×10^{-4} A
   f) 8 900 000 μA or 8.9×10^6 μA
3. a) voltage = current x resistance
   b) $V = IR$
   c) V is in volts, V
      I is in amps, A
      R is in ohms, Ω
4. a) The ratio stays constant.
   b) The current increases.
5. a) 12 Ω
   b) 38 Ω
   c) 200 Ω

6. a) 0.023 A
   b) 4.5×10^{-3} A or 4.5 mA
   c) 0.01 A
7. a) 15 V
   b) 1.5 V
   c) 7.5 V
8. 1.5×10^7 Ω
9. 1.2×10^{-3} A or 1.2 mA
10. 35 V
11. a)

Resistor	Resistance (Ω)	Current
R_1	5	3.2 A
R_2	250	0.064 A
R_3	400	40 mA
R_4	1500	10.7 mA

   b) 16 V
12. a) 75 Ω
    b) 1.8×10^{-4} A
    c) 75 V
    d) 100 Ω
13. a) i) 18 V
       ii) 60 mA
    b) 300 Ω
14. a) 4480 Ω
    b) 140 Ω
15. a) 6 Ω
    b) 2 A
    c) 2 A
    d) i) 8 V
       ii) 4 V
    e) i) 1.33 A
       ii) 0.67 A
16. a) 4 A
    b) i) 2.67A
       ii) 1.33 A
17. a) 2 A
    b) 1.33 A
    c) 0.67 A
18. a) i) 0.5 A
       ii) 0.5 A
    b) i) 0.33 A
       ii) 0.17 A
19. a) 0.125 A
    b) 0.375 A

Potential dividers   **(page 50)**

1. a) V_1 9 V V_2 6 V
    b) V_1 5 V V_2 7 V
    c) V_1 3.6 V V_2 2.4 V
    d) V_1 18 V V_2 6 V
    e) V_1 4.95 V V_2 7.05 V
    f) V_1 46.8 V V_2 3.2 V
2. a) V_1 3 V R_1 1 kΩ
    b) V_1 9 V R_1 3 Ω
    c) V_1 4.8 V R_1 40 Ω
    d) V_1 10.8 V R_1 6 kΩ
    e) V_1 25 V R_1 8 kΩ
    f) V_1 0.9 V R_1 8.3 Ω
3. a) 0 V
    b) 18 V
    c) 9 V
4. a) i) 0 V
      ii) 6 V
     iii) 3 V
      iv) 2 V
    b) 15 kΩ
5. a) 4 V
    b) 2.2 V
6. a) V_1 16 V R_1 2.4 kΩ
    b) V_1 30 V R_1 5.4 kΩ
    c) V_1 73 V R_1 175 Ω

7.

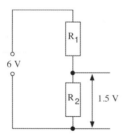

value of R_1 must be
3 times value of R_2
$R_1 = 3R_2$

6 V

R_1

R_2 1.5 V

8.

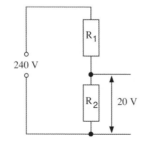

value of R_1 must be
11 times value of R_2
$R_1 = 11R_2$

240 V

R_1

R_2 20 V

Electric charge and electrical current
                                        (page 54)

1. a) charge = current x time
    b) $Q = It$
    c) Q is in coulombs, C
        I is in amps, A
        t is in seconds, s
2. a) 240 C
    b) 90 C
    c) 150 C
3. a) 0.75 A
    b) 12 A
    c) 25 A
4. a) 80 s
    b) 50 s
    c) 250 s
5.   3.3 A
6.   21 000 s
7.   2520 C
8. a) 1500 C
    b) 9.4 x 10^{21}
9. a) 72 C
    b) 4.5 x 10^{20}
10. a) 4.16 A
    b) 12 480 C
    c) 7.8 x 10^{22}

Electrical power and energy   (page 56)

1. a) power = energy / time
   b) $P = E/t$
   c) P is in watts, W
       E is in joules, J
       t is in seconds, s
2. a) 60 J
   b) 5000 J
   c) 0.02 J
3. a) 60 W
   b) 2000 W
   c) 400 W
4. a) 45 000 J
   b) 2.16×10^6 J
   c) 6.9×10^5 J
5. a) 300 s
   b) 6000 s
   c) 60 s
6.   9 J
7.   1000 W
8.   840 s
9. a) 4.3×10^{13} J
   b) i) 1.2×10^{14} J
      ii) 3.3×10^6 kg

Electrical power, current and voltage (page 58)

1. a) power = current x voltage
   b) $P = IV$
   c) P is in watts, W
       I is in amps, A
       V is in volts, V
2. a) 690 W
   b) 0.225 W
   c) 2990 W
3. a) 6.5 A
   b) 4.2 mA
   c) 30 A
4. a) 12 V
   b) 250 V
   c) 3 V
5.   4500 V
6.   9.6 W
7.   13 A

Electrical power, current and resistance (page 59)

1. a) power = (current)² x resistance
   b) $P = I^2R$
   c) P is in watts, W
       I is in amps, A
       R is in ohms, Ω
2. a) 80 W
   b) 0.026 W
   c) 6.75×10^6 W or 6.75 MW
   d) 0.45 W
3. a) 15 Ω
   b) 6 Ω
   c) 8.3×10^7 Ω
   d) 12 Ω
4. a) 0.2 A
   b) 6.3 A
   c) 13 A
   d) 8.6 A
5. a) 4.8×10^{-3} W or 4.8 mW
   b) 48 W
6.   60 W
7.   5.1 A

Electrical power, voltage and resistance (page 60)

1. a) power = (voltage)² / resistance
   b) $P = V^2/R$
   c) P is in watts, W
       V is in volts, V
       R is in ohms, Ω
2. a) 80 W
   b) 12 W
   c) 9.2×10^{-5} W
3. a) 4.8 Ω
   b) 21 Ω
   c) 0.75 Ω
4. a) 100 V
   b) 72 V
   c) 235 V
5.   3.6 Ω
6.   35 W
7.   300 V

Mixed electricity problems (i) (page 61)

1. a) 7.2 W
   b) 25 920 J
2. a) 5 A
   b) 2.8 Ω
3. a) i) 3 A
      ii) 1 A
   b) i) 2 Ω
      ii) 6 Ω
   c) 3600 J or 3.6 kJ
4. a) i) 1.5 A
      ii) 0.37 A
      iii) 8.7 A
   b) i) 2435 W
      ii) 550 kJ
5. a) i) 2 A
      ii) 3 A
   b) i) 3 Ω
      ii) 2 Ω
   c) i) 5 A
      ii) 12 V
   d) 2.4 Ω
6. a) 3 kW
   b) 18 Ω
   c) 13 A
7. 125 s
8. a) 6.5 kW
   b) 28 A
   c) 8.3 Ω
9. a) 9 W
   b) 16 Ω
   c) 0.75 A
   d) 6750 C
10. a) 6613 W
    b) 6×10^7 J
11. a) 0.19 Ω
    b) 373 s
12. a) 2939 W
    b) 13 A
13. a) 1172 W
    b) 94 V
    c) 4.2×10^6 J
    d) 45 000 C

Mixed electricity problems (ii) (page 64)

1. a) 0.75 A
   b) 450 C
   c) 160 minutes
2. a) i) 50 Ω   0.4 V
         300 Ω   2.4 V
         600 Ω   4.8 V
      ii) 7.6 V
   b) i) 50 Ω 3.2×10^{-3} W
         300 Ω 19.2×10^{-3} W
         600 Ω 38.4×10^{-3} W
      ii) 60.8 mW
   c) 18.24 J
   d) 2.4 C
3. a) i) 50 Ω   0.72 A
         300 Ω   0.12 A
         600 Ω   0.06 A
      ii) 0.9 A
   b) i) 50 Ω   25.92 W
         300 Ω   4.32 W
         600 Ω   2.16 W
      ii) 32.4 W
   c) 9720 J
   d) 270 C
4. a) 21.2 V
   b) 6.6 Ω
   c) 0.42 A
   d) 1.2 W
5. a) 36 V
   b) 4 Ω
   c) 8 Ω
   d) 6 Ω
   e) 6 A
6. a) i) 0.5 A
      ii) 6 V
      iii) 3 W
   b) i) 0.33 A
      ii) 3 V
      iii) 1 W
   c) i) 0.17 A
      ii) 3 V
      iii) 0.5 W

7. a) i) 0.5 A
   ii) 8 V
   iii) 4 W
   b) i) 0.33 A
   ii) 10 V
   iii) 3.3 W
   c) i) 0.17 A
   ii) 10 V
   iii) 1.7 W
8. a) i) 24 V
   ii) 12 V
   b) i) R = V/I = 12/2 = 6 Ω
   ii) 3 Ω
   c) i) 48 W
   ii) 48 W

Fuses (page 67)

1. a) 3 A
   b) 15 A
   c) 5 A
   d) 50 A
   e) 10 A
   f) 3 A

Domestic electricity (page 68)

1. a) 12 kWh
   b) 0.875 kWh
   c) 0.25 kWh
   d) 1.65 kWh
2. a) 13.7 kWh
   b) 7.9 kWh
   c) 2.2 kWh
   d) 19.2 kWh
3. a) £1.24
   b) £0.15
   c) £0.04
   d) £0.12
   e) £0.26
   f) £1.70

Electronics (page 69)

1. 122 Ω
2. 450 Ω
3. 100 Ω
4. a) 225 Ω
   b) 800 Ω
   c) 140 Ω
   d) 500 Ω
5. a) 4 V
   b) 200 Ω
6. a) i) 4.6 V
   ii) 1.4 V
   b) i) 2.25 V
   ii) 3.75 V
7. a) 5 V
   b) 1.2 V
8. a) i)

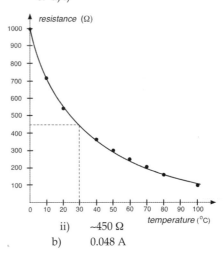

   ii) ~450 Ω
   b) 0.048 A

9. a) i)

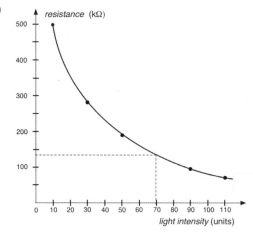

     ii)   ~133 kΩ

     b) 2.1×10^{-8} A or 21 µA

10. a) i)   5.9 V

     ii)   0.1 V

     b) i)   4.2 V

     ii)   1.8 V

11. a)   3 V

     b)   1.2 V

Switching circuits   (page 73)

1.   9000 Ω or 9 kΩ

2. a)   5.4 V

     b)   3 V

3. a) i)   0 V

     ii)   unlit

     b) i)   5 V

     ii)   lit

4. a)   0.6 V

     b)   2 V

5. a)   1 V

     b)   5 V

6.   200 Ω

PROPERTIES OF MATTER

Specific heat capacity (i)   (page 76)

1. a) heat = specific heat capacity
        x mass
        x temperature change

    b) $E_h = cm\Delta t$

    c) E_h is in joules, J
        c is in joules per kilogram per
        degree Celsius, J kg^{-1} $^{\circ}$C^{-1}
        m is in kilograms, kg
        Δt is in degrees Celsius, $^{\circ}$C

2. a) 19.2 kJ
    b) 57.6 kJ

3.   836 kJ

4. a) 900 J kg^{-1} $^{\circ}$C^{-1}
    b) aluminium

5.   3.4 kg

6.   353 $^{\circ}$C

7. a) 469 $^{\circ}$C
    b) 72 $^{\circ}$C

8. a) 244 kJ
    b) 1920 J

9. a) 387 J kg^{-1}$^{\circ}$C^{-1}
    b) copper

10.   50 $^{\circ}$C

11.   60 $^{\circ}$C

12.   650 $^{\circ}$C

Specific heat capacity (ii)   (page 78)

1.   57 $^{\circ}$C

2. a) 1.65 x 10^6 J or 1.65 MJ
    b) i) 220 s
       ii) In practice, it takes longer as
           some of the energy supplied
           is lost to the surroundings.

3.   3.4 kg

4. a) i) 95 kJ
       ii) 298 kJ
       iii) 393 kJ
    b) 262 s

5. a) 271 kJ
    b) 941 s

6. a) 628 kJ
    b) 833 $^{\circ}$C

7. a) 2360 J kg^{-1} $^{\circ}$C^{-1}
    b) alcohol

Latent heat (i)   (page 80)

1. a) heat = specific latent heat
        of fusion / evaporation
        x mass

    b) $E_h = mL$

    c) E_h is in joules, J
        m is in kilograms, kg
        L is in joules per kilogram,
        J kg^{-1}

2. a) 1.67 x 10^6 J or 1670 kJ
    b) 1.8 x 10^4 J or 18 kJ
    c) 7.9 x 10^4 J or 79 kJ

3. a) 8.3 x 10^7 J or 83 MJ
    b) 1.13 x 10^6 J or 1.13 MJ
    c) 5.8 x 10^4 J or 58 kJ

4. a) 3.34 x 10^4 J or 33.4 kJ
    b) 4.52 x 10^5 J or 452 kJ

5.   5.4 x 10^4 J or 54 kJ

6.   8.4 x 10^5 J or 840 kJ

7.   0.4 kg or 400 g

8.   0.05 kg or 50 g

Latent heat (ii)   **(page 81)**

1.   674 g
2.   705 g
3. a) i) 1×10^6 J   or   1MJ
       ii) 1.3×10^6 J   or   1.3 MJ
      iii) 6.8×10^6 J   or   6.8 MJ
     b) 9.1×10^6 J   or   9.1 MJ
4. a) i)   200 kJ
       ii)   766 J
      iii)   2240 kJ
     b)   3206 kJ
5.   439 kJ
6.   225 kJ
7. a)   The wax is melting.
     b)   18 750 J kg^{-1}
8. a) i)   ~8 °C
       ii)   ~70 °C
     b)   60 000 J kg^{-1}
     c)   ~387 J kg^{-1} °C^{-1}
9. a)   29 J
     b)   226 J
     c)   Much more energy is transferred to the skin when the steam changes to liquid water.
10.   2.6 m
11. a) i)   103 kJ
        ii)   187 kJ
      b)   2000 s
      c)   All the energy was removed from the liquid ice cream and none from the surroundings.
12. a)   401 kJ
      b)   501 s

Pressure   **(page 85)**

1. a)   pressure
        = force / surface area
     b) $P = F/A$
     c) P is in Pascals, Pa or N m^{-2}
        F is in Newtons, N
        A is in square metres, m^2
2. a)   2.5 Pa
     b)   750 Pa
     c)   7000 Pa
3. a)   9600 N
     b) 1.2×10^8 N
     c) 6.5×10^2 N
4. a)   1.2 m^2
     b)   20 m^2
     c)   8.4 m^2
5.   5400 N
6. 1.92×10^5 N
7.   5400 kPa or 5.4×10^6 Pa
8. 9.8×10^{-8} m^2

The gas laws: pressure and volume
(page 86)

1. $P_1V_1 = P_2V_2$

2. a)
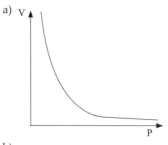

    b)
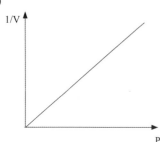

3. a) 6.4×10^5 Pa
    b) 8×10^4 Pa
4. a) 15 m^3
    b) The temperature is constant.
5. a) i) 0.32 m^3
       ii) 0.53 m^3
    b) i) 0.64 atmospheres
       ii) 3.2 atmospheres
6. a) 500 mm
    b) i) 3.2×10^5 Pa
       ii) 1.6×10^6 Pa

The gas laws: volume and temperature
(page 88)

1. a) $V_1/T_1 = V_2/T_2$
    b) Kelvin scale

2. a)
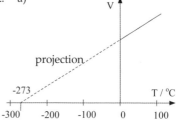

    b)
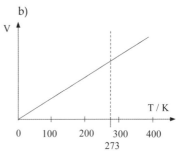

3. a) 273 K
    b) 300 K
    c) 373 K
    d) 200 K
    e) 346 K
    f) 123 K
4. a) 27 °C
    b) -200 °C
    c) - 273 °C
    d) 327 °C
    e) -120 °C
    f) 627 °C
5.   27 K
6. a) 200 litres
    b) 50 litres
    c) 150 litres
    d) 91 litres

7. a) 150 K
    b) 600 K
    c) 390 K
    d) 252 K
8. a) 4.4 m^3
    b) 8 m^3
    c) 5.6 m^3
    d) 2.6 m^3
9.   455 K
10. a) 0.36 m^3
    b) The pressure is constant.

4. a) 250 K
    b) 135 K
    c) 180 K
    d) 375 K
5. a) 184 kPa
    b) 141 kPa
    c) 109 kPa
    d) 200 kPa
6. a) 167 °C
    b) -53 °C
    c) 387 °C
    d) 343 °C
7.   1.2 x 10^5 Pa
8. a) i) 72 °C
       ii) 62 kN m^{-2}
    b) The volume is constant.

The gas laws: pressure and temperature
(page 90)

1. a) $P_1/T_1 = P_2/T_2$
    b) Kelvin scale
2. a)

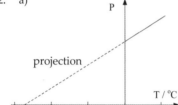

    b)

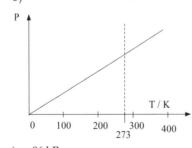

3. a) 96 kPa
    b) 12 kPa
    c) 33 kPa
    d) 52 kPa

General gas equation   (page 92)

1. $P_1V_1/T_1 = P_2V_2/T_2$
2.   120 litres
3.   71 kPa
4.   2100 K
5.   1200 m^3
6.   50 °C
7.   120 m^3
8.   207 °C
9.   The pressure is six times atmospheric pressure.

Mixed gas laws problems   (page 93)

1.   -3 °C
2.   2000 litres
3.   100 °C
4.   2.31 x 10^5 Pa
5.   168 kPa
6.   234 °C
7.   0.12 m^3
8.   313 °C

WAVES

Some wave parameters   (page 94)

1. a) Distance from the rest position to the top of a crest or bottom of a trough.
   b) a
2. a) Distance between crest on one wave to the crest on the next wave.
   b) λ (lambda)
3. a) Number of waves that pass a point in one second.
   b) f
   c) hertz, Hz
4. a) wave period = 1/ frequency
   b) T
   c) seconds, s
5. a) i) 0.3 m
      ii) 10 mm
   b) i) 0.5 m
      ii) 0.3 m
6. a) 6.5 Hz
   b) 0.15 s
7. a) 20 Hz
   b) 0.05 s
8. a) i) 2 m
      ii) 1.5 m
   b) i) 1.5 Hz
      ii) 0.67 s
9. 7 Hz
10. a) i) 5 mm
       ii) 4 mm
    b) i) 6000 Hz
       ii) 1.7×10^{-4} s
11. a) 18 m
    b) i) 0.2 Hz
       ii) 5 s
12. a) i) 0.02 m
       ii) 0.36 m
    b) i) 1.2×10^6 Hz or 1.2 MHz
       ii) 8.3×10^{-7} s
13. a) 0.5 m
    b) 0.75 Hz

Wave speed (i)   (page 97)

1. a) wave speed = distance / time
   b) $s = d/t$
   c) s is in metres per second, m s^{-1}
      d is in metres, m
      t is in seconds, s
2. 15 s
3. 1224 m
4. 338 m s^{-1}
5. 0.026 s
6. 3.4 km
7. a) 2142 km/h
   b) 202 s
8. a) 5100 m
   b) 1.8×10^{10} m
9. 500 s
10. 75 m
11. a) 343 m s^{-1}
    b) 8×10^{-5} s
12. a) 0.53 s
    b) 0.024 s
13. a) 272 m
    b) 136 m
14. a) 1800 m
    b) 750 m
15. 4.7 cm

Wave speed (ii)   **(page 99)**

1. a)   wave speed =   frequency
                       x wavelength
     b) $s = f\lambda$
     c) s is in metres per second, m s^{-1}
           f is in Hertz, Hz
           λ is in metres, m
2. a)   76.8 m s^{-1}
     b)   6750 m s^{-1}
     c)   1190 m s^{-1}
3. a)   10 m
     b) 7×10^{-3} m
     c)   0.2 m
4. a)   6.5 Hz
     b)   120 Hz
     c)   75 Hz
5. 1.5×10^{6} Hz   or   1.5 MHz
6.   30 m s^{-1}
7. 6.7×10^{-7} m
8.   0.045 m s^{-1}
9.   5 m

Mixed wave problems   **(page 100)**

1. a)   70 Hz
     b)   2.1 m s^{-1}
2. a)   7.5 m s^{-1}
    b) i)   30 Hz
      ii)   0.033 s
3. a)   1.2 m
     b)   0.6 Hz
     c)   0.72 m s^{-1}
4. a)   40 m s^{-1}
    b) i)   500 Hz
      ii) 2×10^{-3} s
5. a)   0.05 Hz
     b)   0.35 m s^{-1}
6. a) 1.1×10^{-6} s   or   1.1 μs
    b) i)   2700 m s^{-1}
      ii)   54 km
7. a) 3.7×10^{-3} s
    b) i)   0.0243 ms^{-1}
      ii)   7.29 m

8. a)   2000 Hz
    b) i)   150 m s^{-1}
      ii)   0.2 s
9. a)   0.25 m s^{-1}
     b)   7 Hz
     c)   0.036 m
10.   0.05 s
11. 4×10^{-6} s
12.   1440 m
13. 1.2×10^{6} m
14. a) i) 1.5×10^{-3} m
      ii) 3.1×10^{14} Hz
     b) 2.25×10^{-3} m

The electromagnetic spectrum (page 102)

1. a)   3.2 m
     b)   radio and television
2. a) 7.5×10^{-9} m
     b)   ultraviolet
3. a) 6×10^{15} Hz
     b)   visible
4. a) 6×10^{17} Hz
     b)   x-rays
5. 1.7×10^{20} s

RADIATION

Activity (page 103)
1. a) The activity of a radioactive source in which one nucleus decays per second.
   b) Bq
2. a) 3600 Bq
   b) 3100 Bq
3. a) 9600
   b) 4.5×10^9
4. a) 270 s
   b) 20 s

Absorbed dose (page 104)
1. a) absorbed dose = energy / mass
   b) $D = E/m$
   c) D is in grays, Gy
      E is in joules, J
      m is in kilograms, kg
2. a) 0.03 kg or 30 g
   b) 0.45 kg or 450 g
3. a) 0.18 Gy
   b) 0.42 Gy
4. a) 2.94×10^{-3} J
   b) 0.001 J
5. worker **A** 2.4 mGy
   worker **B** 2.1 mGy
   so worker **A** has the greater absorbed dose

Equivalent dose (page 105)
1. a) equivalent dose = absorbed dose x radiation weighting factor
   b) $H = D \times w_r$
   c) H is in sieverts, Sv
      D is in grays, Gy
      w_r is a number
2. 450 µSv
3. a) 280 µSv
   b) 13 440 µSv or 13.44 mSv
4. a) 1950 µSv or 1.95 mSv
   b) 120 mSv
5. a) 41 µGy or 0.041 mGy
   b) 195 µGy
6. a) 1.8
   b) 2.3
7. a) 650 µSv
   b) 320 µSv
   c) 2620 µSv
   d) 500 µSv
8. a) 3
   b) slow neutrons
9. total is 47 mSv so within limit
   (20 mSv from fast neutrons
     10 mSv from alpha
     9 mSv from slow neutrons
     8 mSv from gamma)
10. a) 700 µSv
    b) 16.8 mSv h^{-1}
11. 5.4×10^{-6} J
12. 0.36 Sv

Half-life

(page 107)

1. a) 10 kBq
    b) 75 MBq
    c) 300 MBq
2. a) 272 kBq
    b) 224 MBq
    c) 288 MBq
3. a) 300 days
    b) 9 hours
    c) 150 s
4. a) 6 hours
    b) 2 days
    c) 2 s
5. a) 1/4
    b) 1/32
6. a) 7 years
    b) 14 years
7. 9.6 mSv
8. 300 kBq
9. a) 1.25 hours
    b) 15 mins
10. a) 5 years
    b) 9 hours
11. 272 kBq
12. a) 18 minutes
    b) 40 days
13. a) i) 1200 kBq
    ii) ~32 hours
    b) ~16 hours
14. a)

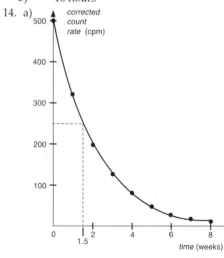

b) ~1.5 weeks
15. a) 5 days
    b) 8 hours
16. ~4.5 years
17. a) i) 30 counts per minute
    ii)

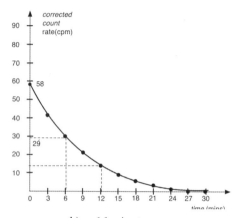

b) ~6.1 minutes

Significant figures

(page 111)

1. 30 m s^{-1} (2 significant figures)
2. 2.2 W (2 significant figures)
3. 8.2 m s^{-2} (2 significant figures)
4. 150 kg (2 significant figures)
5. 4.7 m s^{-1} (2 significant figures)
6. 310 N (2 significant figures)
7. 16 000 J or 16 kJ
    (2 significant figures)
8. 20 500 J or 20.5 kJ
    (3 significant figures)
9. 14 000 J or 14 kJ
    (2 significant figures)
10. 0.33 m^3 (2 significant figures)
11. 86.7 K (3 significant figures)